THE
Quiz Kids
BLUE BOOK

THE SAALFIELD PUBLISHING COMPANY
AKRON, OHIO   **NEW YORK**

Publishers for the Children

SCORE BOARD

QUIZ KIDS   93
YOUR SCORE _____
MY SCORE _____

Quiz Kids

POPULAR QUIZ—NUMBER ONE

Look in a Book for This

QUIZ 1. If flyleaves have nothing to do with entomology, where can they be found?

Answer on page 1, Blue Section

Where Do They Grow?

QUIZ 2. Do the following items grow in a patch, a grove, or an orchard:

       (a) orange
       (b) peach
       (c) potato

Answer on page 1, Blue Section

Schools

QUIZ 3. A grammar school teaches more than grammar, while a normal school is not the place to train for the average life, but for a specialized profession. What is that profession?

Answer on page 1, Blue Section

Judas

QUIZ 4. Judas was the betrayer of Jesus. For how much money did he sell out?

Answer on page 1, Blue Section

English Expressions

QUIZ 5. "Tram" is the English word for streetcar. What is the American word for the English "pram"?

Answer on page 1, Blue Section

Body Parts

QUIZ 6. Everyday terms such as drum, pump, and box are applied to parts of the human body. Name them.

Answer on page 1, Blue Section

A Sterling Question

QUIZ 7. We hope you never get fooled on the difference between sterling silver and silver plate. Just to make sure, we'll ask you to define them both.

Answer on page 1, Blue Section

Best Scores

QUIZ 8. The best possible score on an eighteen-hole golf course is 18 strokes. What is the best score in a set of tennis?

Answer on page 1, Blue Section

Even Exchange

QUIZ 9. If you had a certificate that you could take to the bank and exchange for one-tenth of ten dollars, what kind of a certificate might you have?

Answer on page 1, Blue Section

A Hair-raising Question!

QUIZ 10. The following persons, one a character in mythology and the other in the Bible, were both famous because of one physical feature. What was it?
(a) Medusa
(b) Samson

Answer on page 1, Blue Section

QUIZ KIDS

POPULAR QUIZ—NUMBER TWO

Oh, Louella!

QUIZ 1.   Louella Parsons and Luella Gear are both important in the field of entertainment. Tell who each is.

Score 5 points for each.

Answer on page 1, Blue Section

Think! Think!

QUIZ 2.   In the word "dodo," the name of a bird now extinct, both syllables are pronounced and spelled alike. Each of the following phrases defines a word whose two syllables are the same. Give them.

        (a) a kind of drum

        (b) a low sound

        (c) a dance

Score 10 points for 2 out of 3.

Answer on page 1, Blue Section

Types of Follies

QUIZ 3.   You wouldn't be likely to confuse Flo Ziegfeld's "Follies" with "Seward's Folly." Describe both.

Score 5 points for each.

Answer on page 1, Blue Section

Same Name, Same Field!

QUIZ 4.   A family name is not all that Charles G. Norris, Kathleen Norris, and Frank Norris have alike. Tell what other common bond they have.

Answer on page 1, Blue Section

(3)

The Middle Ages

QUIZ 5. Historians have termed a certain period in history the Middle Ages as a convenience in discussing the period. Give a rough estimate of the centuries that the Middle Ages encompass.

Answer on page 1, Blue Section

Onomatopoeia?

QUIZ 6. Onomatopoeia is the formation of words in imitation of natural sounds. Name at least two such words that you use or read frequently.

Answer on page 2, Blue Section

Tempus Fugit

QUIZ 7. In the course of its speedy flight, how many times does the minute hand pass the hour hand on a clock from noon to midnight?

Answer on page 2, Blue Section

Most Heavily Populated

QUIZ 8. The United States of America is a great country with a large population. Nevertheless there are three countries having larger populations than the United States. Name at least two of them.

Answer on page 2, Blue Section

The Answer Is in the Stars

QUIZ 9. If Orion, the mighty warrior constellation, were thirsty, what could he find to drink, and from what utensil could he drink?

Answer on page 2, Blue Section

Postage to Alaska

QUIZ 10. Can you send a message to Alaska for a penny?

Answer on page 2, Blue Section

QUIZ KIDS

POPULAR QUIZ—NUMBER THREE

Getting the Towns

Quiz 1. It isn't necessary for you to review your geography in order to identify the following towns. What are they?

   (a) Boys Town
   (b) Big Town
   (c) Boom Town

Score 10 points for 2 out of 3.

Answer on page 2, Blue Section

Name the Animal

Quiz 2. Answer this one with the name of an animal:

If you shed fake tears, pretending they're real,
What's the name for such tears that you don't really feel?

Answer on page 2, Blue Section

Concentrate!

Quiz 3. A train leaves New York for Chicago traveling 50 miles an hour at 8:00 P.M., E.S.T., and another train leaves Chicago for New York traveling 40 miles an hour at 9:00 P.M., C.S.T. Which train will be nearest to New York when they pass each other?

Answer on page 2, Blue Section

The Golden Touch

Quiz 4. Who was the mythological king that had a gift all of us might wish for, that of turning all he touched into gold?

Answer on page 2, Blue Section

Calling All Joes!

QUIZ 5. You remember barefoot, bashful Joe of the song "School Days." Give the surname of three other famous Joes that can be described as follows:

    (a) a former United States Ambassador to England
    (b) a center-fielder for the New York Yankees
    (c) a popular character in a syndicated comic strip

Score 10 points for 2 out of 3.

Answer on page 2, Blue Section

Wind Instruments

QUIZ 6. Musical instruments that are sounded by wind blown from the lungs are known as wood-wind and brass-wind instruments. What two musical instruments sounded by wind are in neither of these classifications?

Answer on page 2, Blue Section

It's All Greek

QUIZ 7. *Dia* sometimes means "between"; *legein* means "to speak or discourse"; but the words "dialogue" and "dialect," combining the word *dia* with different forms of the word *legein*, have different meanings. What are their meanings?
Score 5 points for each.

Answer on page 2, Blue Section

Sport Terminology

QUIZ 8. Every sport has its own terminology. Tell what sport uses the following phrases, and give the meaning of two out of three of the terms:

    (a) the pill
    (b) a muff
    (c) a daisy cutter

Answer on page 2, Blue Section

Make One Word

QUIZ 9. This can be done without pencil and paper: form one word from the words "new door."

Answer on page 2, Blue Section

Songs About Animals

QUIZ 10. Most popular songs are about "love," "moon," and "June." Name songs written about the following animals:

    (a) a donkey
    (b) a bull
    (c) a fox

Score 10 points for 2 out of 3.

Answer on page 2, Blue Section

TELL-WHO QUIZ

1. _____ served but one month of his term as President of the United States.
2. _____ is called the "Hoosier Poet."
3. _____ made the character "Babbitt" famous.
4. _____ built a palace with the aid of a lamp.
5. _____ was the Roman orator, soldier, and statesman that killed himself by falling on his own sword.
6. _____ was the famous American inventor that includes the mimeograph along with his many other inventions.
7. _____ was President of the United States in 1902.
8. _____ wrote *Canterbury Tales*.
9. _____ attended the Boston Tea Party.
10. _____ attended the Mad Tea Party.
11. _____ painted *The Last Supper*.
12. _____ was a beautiful youth who fell in love with his own reflection in a pool, and was turned into a flower.
13. _____ was the Indian wife of one of the members of the Lewis and Clark Expedition. She is sometimes called the "Bird Woman."

Answer on page 3, Blue Section

(7)

QUIZ KIDS

POPULAR QUIZ—NUMBER FOUR

Give an Honest Answer

QUIZ 1. George Washington and Abraham Lincoln, two of our great Presidents, were noted for one identical characteristic. It is used in the nickname given to one of them and in a legend told about the other. What is this characteristic?

Answer on page 3, Blue Section

A Nickname

QUIZ 2. You know that one of the National League star players was nicknamed "Dizzy" (Dean). What prime minister of England under Queen Victoria was also named "Dizzy"?

Answer on page 3, Blue Section

Popular Tune

QUIZ 3. Name an old popular dance tune which can be expressed by the twentieth letter of the alphabet followed by two numerals.

Answer on page 3, Blue Section

A New Word

QUIZ 4. Billy Rose, through the title of his show at the World's Fair, added what new word to our language?

Answer on page 3, Blue Section

Figures

QUIZ 5. If you were to receive the product of $1.10 times 1.10, how much money would be due you?

Answer on page 3, Blue Section

(8)

Inside-out Food?

QUIZ 6.   What food, very popular at spectator sports events and circuses, must be turned inside out before eating?

Answer on page 3, Blue Section

Geographical Center

QUIZ 7.   Minnesota is the most northerly State. Florida is the State farthest south. Which State is the geographical center of the United States?

Answer on page 3, Blue Section

Three Words

QUIZ 8.   A donjon is the main tower of a castle. What is:
        (a) a Don Juan
        (b) a dungeon
Score 5 points for each.

Answer on page 3, Blue Section

A Question of Bucks

QUIZ 9.   Gene Buck is a composer. Name two other individuals of that surname, one of whom is a Pulitzer prize winner, author of novels for the most part about China; the other, a famous wild animal hunter who "brings 'em back alive."

Answer on page 3, Blue Section

It Carried "Okies"

QUIZ 10.   In what movie, depicting the migration of hundreds of workers, did an antiquated Hudson truck play an important part?

Answer on page 3, Blue Section

QUIZZICAL QUIZ NUMBER ONE

On which side of your house would you plant sunflowers?

Answer on page 31, Blue Section

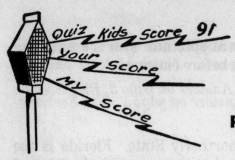

QUIZ KIDS

POPULAR QUIZ—NUMBER FIVE

The Time, Please!

QUIZ 1. If a new speed airplane were built which could fly around the world in twenty-four hours, and an aviator were to start in it from New York at noon, what time would it be when he flew over China?

Answer on page 3, Blue Section

A Relative?

QUIZ 2. If you had a stepsister and a half sister, how would each be related to you?

Answer on page 4, Blue Section

Parlor Games

QUIZ 3. If you used the following items in games, what three parlor games would you play?

    (a) dice and checkers (both are used in this game)
    (b) knights and castles
    (c) marbles

Score 10 points for 2 out of 3.

Answer on page 4, Blue Section

Things in Common

QUIZ 4. Henry Clay, Samuel J. Tilden, and Wendell Willkie had one experience in common. What is it?

Answer on page 4, Blue Section

(10)

Main Line

Quiz 5. "The Main Line" in Philadelphia has been the subject of two recent important movie releases. Name at least one of them.

Answer on page 4, Blue Section

No Car?   No Wife?

Quiz 6. Due to government rules rather than to economic conditions, one group of men in this country can have neither wives nor automobiles. Who are they?

Answer on page 4, Blue Section

It Was Made into a Movie

Quiz 7. The eclipse of the sun was an important episode in a book by an American humorist. Name the book and the author. Score 5 points for each.

Answer on page 4, Blue Section

Animal Talk

Quiz 8. Dogs bark. Kittens purr. What are the sounds that the following animals make:

(a) wolves
(b) donkeys
(c) turkeys

Score 10 points for 2 out of 3.

Answer on page 4, Blue Section

Names for Mistakes

Quiz 9. In tennis a certain kind of misplay is called "a fault"; in basketball we speak of "fouls." What is the term applied to a misplay in baseball? Don't err on this question.

Answer on page 4, Blue Section

M-m-m, Food!

QUIZ 10. "Peach Melba" and "Chicken Tetrazzini" are foods named after famous personages whose talents were in the same field. Who were they?

Answer on page 4, Blue Section

WHAT QUIZ

1. What is the "saros period" and how long is it?
2. What are the commissioned grades in the United States Army?
3. What is found at the ends of the Greenwich Meridian?
4. What conveyance is the theme of the poem "The Deacon's Masterpiece"?
5. What city did Joshua conquer by blowing trumpets?
6. What physical defect is identified with the mice that chased the farmer's wife?
7. What fish begins its life cycle in a fresh-water stream and migrates to the sea?
8. What is the practical use of canaries in peace time and in war time?
9. What scientist is intimately connected with the book *On the Origin of Species by Means of Natural Selection?*
10. What was the first radio station in the United States?
11. What great beloved American actor and wit was not born in the United States, nor did he die in any one of the forty-eight States?
12. What point of the compass lies exactly halfway between north and north-east?
13. What cities are found at the ends of the Erie Canal?
14. What State uses only the letters S I M P in its eleven-letter name?
15. What is the Sargasso Sea?
16. What other country may be designated by U. S. A. other than the United States of America?
17. What metal is the best conductor of electricity?
18. What is meant by a cartel?
19. What fish shoots its dinner?

Answers on pages 4 and 5, Blue Section

QUIZ KIDS

POPULAR QUIZ—NUMBER SIX

Under Four Flags

QUIZ 1.   The French flag, the Spanish flag, and the flag of the United States of America have all flown over New Orleans.   This city has been under what fourth flag?

Answer on page 5, Blue Section

The Name Is Jackson

QUIZ 2.   Associate Justice Robert Jackson is making that name famous. Identify the following famous Jacksons:
  (a) the author of *Ramona*
  (b) a President of the United States
Score 10 points for 1 out of 2.

Answer on page 5, Blue Section

Guess Who?

QUIZ 3.   Answer the following descriptions with the names of men, each having the given name of Walter:
  (a) a leader in the field of animated cartoon, originator and producer of "Fantasia"
  (b) a famous Broadway columnist
  (c) an automobile manufacturer

Answer on page 5, Blue Section

Sign Here, Please!

QUIZ 4.   Who was the great American statesman and inventor that signed the Declaration of Independence, the Treaty of Alliance with France, the Treaty of Peace with Great Britain, and the Constitution of the United States?

Answer on page 5, Blue Section

(13)

It's a Metal Too

QUIZ 5. We usually speak of liquid as "running," but there is one element, which though liquid at ordinary temperatures, separates into small globules when poured. What is it?

Answer on page 5, Blue Section

A Little Addition

QUIZ 6. The sum of what three consecutive whole numbers equals 63?

Answer on page 5, Blue Section

Would You Add an "S"?

QUIZ 7. The plural of the word "alumnus" is "alumni." Give the singular of the word "data."

Answer on page 5, Blue Section

He Can't Write

QUIZ 8. What mark would an illiterate man make as his signature?

Answer on page 5, Blue Section

Fighting Words!

QUIZ 9. Man O' War was a famous race horse. What was a Roman man-of-war?

Answer on page 5, Blue Section

Capital Port

QUIZ 10. What was the last open port in Europe in 1941? It is the capital of its country.

Answer on page 5, Blue Section

QUIZZICAL QUIZ NUMBER TWO

The skin of what fruit makes the best slipper?

Answer on page 31, Blue Section

DISASTER AT THE DOCK

You're a reporter covering the "disaster." Look at the drawing for two minutes, turn it over, and write all you remember.

Answer on page 31, Blue Section

QUIZ KIDS
POPULAR QUIZ—NUMBER SEVEN

My Word! Don't You Know?

QUIZ 1. For what throne is Princess Margaret Rose in line of succession?

Answer on page 5, Blue Section

Baa! Such a Question!

QUIZ 2. The following phrases are all from nursery rhymes. What subject do all three of the rhymes concern, and from what rhyme does each come?

 (a) "three bags full"
 (b) "fleece as white as snow"
 (c) "can't tell where to find them"

Answer on page 6, Blue Section

Home of Evangeline

QUIZ 3. Acadie or Acadia was once the name of a part of Canada. What is that section now called?

Answer on page 6, Blue Section

Battle Cries!

QUIZ 4. The catch phrase of the last World War was "Make the world safe for Democracy." What were the "battle cries" of:

 (a) the Spanish-American War
 (b) the Oregon Territory Dispute (1845)

Answer on page 6, Blue Section

Two and Two

QUIZ 5. In order to get this you must be able to put two and two together. How long is it from two-two to two to two, by the hands of the clock?

Answer on page 6, Blue Section

Yes, Your Honor!

QUIZ 6. One of the most famous judges in American history was John Marshall. What highly honored position did he hold from 1801 to 1835?

Answer on page 6, Blue Section

A Timely Question

QUIZ 7. Synonyms for the following phrases are all parts of a watch. For example, to look at a thing squarely is to "face" it. What parts of a watch are synonyms for the following:

        (a) anything not new
        (b) something read by the secretary
        (c) the support of a flower

Score 10 points for 2 out of 3.

Answer on page 6, Blue Section

A Robust Character

QUIZ 8. The name of the author of the books, *Tess of the D'Urbervilles* and *The Return of the Native*, suggests a robust character. What is the author's name?

Answer on page 6, Blue Section

Holiday Colors

QUIZ 9. Color combinations have become symbolic of certain festive holidays. What holidays would you be celebrating if you decorated your table with the following color combinations:

        (a) red and green
        (b) orange and black
        (c) red, white, and blue

Answer on page 6, Blue Section

Big League Names

QUIZ 10. Robbers of the seas, insects, and persons of great size are the descriptive names of major league baseball teams. What are the names of at least two?

Answer on page 6, Blue Section

FIGURE IT OUT

1. A pretty nurse in a ward at a children's hospital walked down the center aisle and gently kissed the 27 babies on her left. Then she walked back again, gently kissing all the babies on her right. How many babies did the nurse kiss?

2. A boy had a great many marbles. He decided to put them in a glass jar at 12 o'clock, and he filled it in exactly 30 minutes. He put in one marble the first minute, 2 marbles the second minute, 4 marbles the third minute, and so on, doubling the number of marbles each minute. How many minutes did it take him to get the jar one-quarter full?

3. There is the old question that says "would you rather get $1,000 for thirty days' work or take a penny the first day, two cents the second, four the third, and so on with the amount doubled each day?" Of course, the latter would be more profitable, meaning a neat profit of $10,736,418.23. This is a new version of that problem. How much would be earned under that plan if $671,088.64 were paid for the last day's work? What would be the total earnings?

4. An elm tree has twenty branches. Each branch has two twigs and there are two acorns on each twig. How many acorns are there on the tree?

5. A baker placed nine doughnuts in a box and gave them to his delivery boy for delivery after marking the number of doughnuts in Roman numerals on the outside of the box. The delivery boy was hungry; he opened the box and ate three of the doughnuts. Then, without making an erasure, he changed the number on the outside of the box to coincide with the number of doughnuts left in the box. How did he do it? He had a pencil, but *no* erasure was made.

Answers on page 6, Blue Section

(18)

QUIZ KIDS

POPULAR QUIZ—NUMBER EIGHT

The South Pole

QUIZ 1.   The regions around the North Pole are called the Arctic Circle. By what name are the regions around the South Pole designated?

Answer on page 6, Blue Section

A Novel

QUIZ 2.   A post-war novel, which started a trend of many more like it, was written by Erich Maria Remarque. It was twice made into highly successful movies.   What was its name?

Answer on page 6, Blue Section

National Symbols

QUIZ 3.   The fleur-de-lis was the symbol of ancient France. What countries do the following symbolize:

      (a) hammer and sickle
      (b) rising sun
      (c) lion

Score 10 points for 2 out of 3.

Answer on page 6, Blue Section

A Friendly Bird

QUIZ 4.   What bird, which is not disturbed by the presence of human beings, is often found around railroad stations and city squares and is fed by kind-hearted individuals?

Answer on page 6, Blue Section

Savings

QUIZ 5. If you saved a dime a day in 1940, and did the same thing through 1941, how much would you have saved at the end of this two-year period? Watch out!

Answer on page 6, Blue Section

Black and White

QUIZ 6. Black and white are difficult words to define, usually being described in simple terms of contrast; i.e., black is the opposite of white. Give better definitions.
Score 5 points for each.

Answer on page 7, Blue Section

Too Hot to Handle

QUIZ 7. Name two radio comedians whose names suggest that they are too hot to handle.

Answer on page 7, Blue Section

Indian Ancestry

QUIZ 8. How many of your ancestors would have to be Indians or have Indian blood in order for you to be one-sixth Indian? Be careful of this one!

Answer on page 7, Blue Section

L C? M T?

QUIZ 9. The letters K T, when pronounced together, sound like the girl's name Katy. What two letters of the alphabet, when pronounced together, sound like the word for rot or deteriorate?

Answer on page 7, Blue Section

Benito's Talents

QUIZ 10. Benito Mussolini began his career in a field which engaged his talents as a writer rather than his later developed talent of orator. In what profession was he then engaged?

Answer on page 7, Blue Section

QUIZ KIDS

POPULAR QUIZ—NUMBER NINE

Valuable Documents

QUIZ 1. The famous Library of Congress in Washington, D.C. contains many rare original documents. Two of these are extremely important in the history of the origin of the United States. What are they?

Answer on page 7, Blue Section

This "Seams" Hard!

QUIZ 2. If you were to make a baseball, how many seams would you put on it? This is easier than it sounds.

Answer on page 7, Blue Section

A Matter of Terminology

QUIZ 3. Cats are termed feline, cows bovine. What are the following termed:
- (a) horses
- (b) dogs

Answer on page 7, Blue Section

No Guessing!

QUIZ 4. What would you call a unit with nine zeros?

Answer on page 7, Blue Section

Baby Talk!

QUIZ 5. A baby is called "bambino" in Italy. In what country is a baby called "bairn"?

Answer on page 7, Blue Section

Gesundheit!

QUIZ 6. What song title might be expressed as follows: "What the people of the United States say when Uncle Sam sneezes."

Answer on page 7, Blue Section

I Is—

QUIZ 7. Grammar is often mangled in such usage as "he don't" and "I is." However, there are times when "I is" is permissible in the English language. Complete the sentence.

Answer on page 7, Blue Section

The Great Profile

QUIZ 8. "The Great Profile" does not refer to one of the rock carvings at Mt. Rushmore. To what or whom does it belong?

Answer on page 7, Blue Section

Story Book Sisters

QUIZ 9. One of the most famous sets of fictional sisters in the world was Meg, Beth, Jo, and Amy. In what book are they depicted?

Answer on page 7, Blue Section

The Clock Strikes!

QUIZ 10. If a clock is striking one hour behind the time, what time is it when it strikes eleven times more than it should?

Answer on page 7, Blue Section

QUIZZICAL QUIZ NUMBER THREE

A man working in a butcher shop wears a 7⅝ hat; 16 collar; and 36-inch belt. What does he weigh?

Answer on page 31, Blue Section

QUIZ KIDS

POPULAR QUIZ—NUMBER TEN

SCORE BOARD
Quiz Kids _90_
Others ____
Ours ____

Hop This Question!

QUIZ 1. Suppose you have a kangaroo, an elephant, and an eel. Which would you place in a cage labeled "Marsupials"?

Answer on page 7, Blue Section

Famous Last Names

QUIZ 2. These words are the same as last names of famous poets. Complete their names.
- (a) field
- (b) frost
- (c) guest

Answer on page 7, Blue Section

In the Blue Grass State

QUIZ 3. Two men, Presidents at the same time, were born in the same State. Who were they and what was the State?

Answer on page 7, Blue Section

Submarine Machine

QUIZ 4. What device enabled William Beebe to make his extensive underwater observations?

Answer on page 7, Blue Section

Army Garb

QUIZ 5. Blue, gray, and red should remind you of three armies. What were they?

Answer on page 7, Blue Section

Scrambled Quotations

Quiz 6. Unscramble these quotations and name their originators:

(a) "I'd rather be right than carry a big stick."

(b) "Speak softly, but be President."

Answer on page 7, Blue Section

Uncle Tom's Master

Quiz 7. In *Uncle Tom's Cabin*, who was Uncle Tom's cruel overseer?

Answer on page 8, Blue Section

No Galoshes!

Quiz 8. A jacket, hood, and muffler would be a good costume for a cold day. However, they are each parts of an automobile. What are they?

Score 10 points for 2 out of 3.

Answer on page 8, Blue Section

Isn't This Odd?

Quiz 9. What are prime numbers?

Answer on page 8, Blue Section

Hey, Don't Forget This One!

Quiz 10. When is a field of clover like a statesman whose first name was John?

Answer on page 8, Blue Section

QUIZZICAL QUIZ NUMBER FOUR

What is the difference between an old five-dollar bill and a new one?

Answer on page 31, Blue Section

QUIZ KIDS

POPULAR QUIZ—NUMBER ELEVEN

Quiz Kids 93
Yours ____
Mine ____

Poetry

QUIZ 1.   Longfellow's poems are read by all. What famous poet wrote "The Death of Longfellow"?

Answer on page 8, Blue Section

About a War

QUIZ 2.   During the French and Indian War a famous battle was waged on the Heights of Abraham. What was it?

Answer on page 8, Blue Section

The Date Was 1774

QUIZ 3.   What was the Quebec Act?

Answer on page 8, Blue Section

A Mountain out of Place!

QUIZ 4.   Which mountain should not be in this group and why?
- (a) Mt. Columbia
- (b) Mt. Thielson
- (c) Mt. Hood

Answer on page 8, Blue Section

An Old Question

QUIZ 5.   If not for its memory, why might an elephant be compared with Methuselah?

Answer on page 8, Blue Section

(25)

It's not a Balloon!

QUIZ 6. Where would you go to find a puffball?

Answer on page 8, Blue Section

Calling Rachel!

QUIZ 7. Name two famous Rachels other than the one spoken to by Reuben.
Score 5 points for each.

Answer on page 8, Blue Section

How Many?

QUIZ 8. How many rode in the "Charge of the Light Brigade"?

Answer on page 8, Blue Section

A Burning Question

QUIZ 9. "To burn daylight" is an expression meaning to waste time. Give at least two other common expressions beginning with "to burn."

Answer on page 8, Blue Section

There Are Two

QUIZ 10. What races live on the Iberian Peninsula?

Answer on page 8, Blue Section

MIGHT-HAVE-BEEN WANT ADS

Situation Wanted: Gentleman experienced in printing, politics, philosophy, journalism, literature, post office management, inventing, library work, and diplomacy would like employment in any, or all, of these lines. Versatility a specialty.
Address BF, care of *New England Courant.*

For Rent: In heart of Tuscany. Tall edifice, consists of series of six arcades. Decorated with semi-circular arches. Surmounted by belfry, leaning 16 feet out of perpendicular.

Answers on page 8, Blue Section

Quiz Kids Score
90

Your Score

My Score

QUIZ KIDS

POPULAR QUIZ—NUMBER TWELVE

Roman Symbols

QUIZ 1. Give the Roman symbols for the following numerals: 1, 5, 10, 50, 100, 500, and 1,000.

Answer on page 8, Blue Section

Say da Woid!

QUIZ 2. Give the definitions of the following samples of gangster terminology:

        (a) a dip
        (b) a moll
        (c) a mouthpiece

Answer on page 8, Blue Section

Fathom This One!

QUIZ 3. How many dozen would there be if you divided the number of degrees in a circle by the number of feet in a fathom?

Answer on page 8, Blue Section

Identity

QUIZ 4. If you're not cross by this time, identify the following Crosses:

        (a) Southern Cross
        (b) Crossbill
        (c) Milton Cross

Answer on page 9, Blue Section

Do You Have It?

QUIZ 5. What is the answer to the following riddle:

Luke had it before;
Paul had it behind;
Matthew never had it once;
Mrs. Mulligan had it twice in succession;
Dr. Lowell had it before and behind;
And he had it twice as bad behind as before.

Answer on page 9, Blue Section

Delicacies

QUIZ 6. To what countries are the following delicacies attributed and of what do they consist:

(a) *pâté de foie gras*
(b) poi
(c) caviar

Answer on page 9, Blue Section

Question in Rhyme

QUIZ 7. What device is described in the following verse:

A speedy boat without a sail
That swims below just like a whale.

Answer on page 9, Blue Section

They Only Sound Alike!

QUIZ 8. Distinguish between a prie-dieu and a billet-doux.

Answer on page 9, Blue Section

Give the Prefix

QUIZ 9. The words cycle, watt, meter, and gram all add the same prefix: the first when used for a measure of radio wave length; the second when used for measuring electrical consumption; the third for measuring distance; the fourth as a measure of weight. What is the prefix?

Answer on page 9, Blue Section

A "Crying" Matter

QUIZ 10. Give at least two common expressions using the word "cry."

Answer on page 9, Blue Section

THIS-AND-THAT QUIZ

1. Is Paris green used to dye dress fabrics?
2. Of what is rayon made?
3. Is a polygraph a new type of phonograph?
4. Will an iron ball fall faster through water heated to 130 degrees Fahrenheit or water at 30 degrees Fahrenheit?
5. Can any object be wider than it is long?
6. What one color is composed of violet, indigo, blue, green, yellow, orange, and red?
7. Is sodium chloride used to season food?
8. Why does fanning a flame make it burn more intensely?
9. How cold is twice as cold as 10 degrees below zero?
10. Why do gasoline tank trucks have chains dragging on the ground?
11. What is the similarity between fire and rust?
12. What is the abbreviation for the explosive, trinitrotoluene?
13. If a thermometer is held in front of an electric fan, will the breeze cause the mercury to rise, drop, or remain the same?
14. How many inches are in a hand?
15. Would the contents of a can of soup weigh more in an ice box or on the hot stove?
16. If you toss a coin up eight times, and the head comes up each time, what are the chances that the head will come up the ninth time it is tossed?
17. What substances are used to make bronze, glass, and nylon?
18. What are the proper words to describe the effect of weather and air on iron, silver, and copper?
19. Why is an avoirdupois pound heavier than an apothecaries' pound?
20. What is the coldest thing in the world?

Answers on pages 9 and 10, Blue Section

SCRAMBLED PAIRS

How good are you at unscrambling things? Then pair off these drawings. 1 and 8 go together: Ice cream and cake.

Answer on page 31, Blue Section

QUIZ KIDS

POPULAR QUIZ—NUMBER THIRTEEN

A Kingly Question

QUIZ 1. Charles the Great, or Charlemagne, was king of the Franks. What countries were ruled by:

    (a) Frederick the Great

    (b) Peter the Great

Score 5 points for each.

Answer on page 10, Blue Section

My, What a Big Nose!

QUIZ 2. On first reading it sounds improbable, but what animal can scratch its ear with its nose?

Answer on page 10, Blue Section

Greetings

QUIZ 3. What is the method of greeting (as the handshake in America) used by:

    (a) Eskimos

    (b) Nazis

Answer on page 10, Blue Section

Would You?

QUIZ 4. If a drummer were playing the "Star-Spangled Banner" in a parade, and it started to hail, should he run for shelter?

Answer on page 10, Blue Section

Oh, Mr. Postmaster!

QUIZ 5.   Here's one to test your powers of observation:

(a) How many lines are there on a canceled postage stamp?

(b) How are the lines made? Straight? Waved?

Score 5 points for each.

Answer on page 10, Blue Section

Stage and Screen

QUIZ 6.   Name two stage and screen personalities with the same last name.

Answer on page 10, Blue Section

A Mile a Minute

QUIZ 7.   How long will it take a mile-long train running a mile a minute to pass through a tunnel a mile long?

Answer on page 10, Blue Section

International Competition

QUIZ 8.   In what big-league winter game do American teams and Canadian teams give each other strong opposition?

Answer on page 10, Blue Section

Repetition

QUIZ 9.   All the kings of Belgium have had one or the other of two names. What are the names?

Answer on page 10, Blue Section

Army Initials

QUIZ 10.   K. P. stands for Knight of St. Patrick in Great Britain. It is not so impressive when used in the American Army. What is its meaning?

Answer on page 10, Blue Section

QUIZ KIDS

POPULAR QUIZ—NUMBER FOURTEEN

White-Collar Girl

QUIZ 1. What is the name of the white-collar girl who, since a book bearing her name as its title was published, has become the symbol for her group? The book has recently been made into a movie starring Ginger Rogers.

Answer on page 10, Blue Section

These Gates!

QUIZ 2. If the kind of gate that will punish is castigate, what kind of gate will:

        (a) go to a convention
        (b) sail the ocean blue
        (c) be worn in a ring

Score 10 points for 2 out of 3.

Answer on page 10, Blue Section

Put? Cast? Parry?

QUIZ 3. If you were able to put, cast, and parry better than anyone else you knew, in what three sports would you probably excel? Score 10 points for 2 out of 3.

Answer on page 10, Blue Section

This Is a Hard One!

QUIZ 4. Which side of the Rock of Gibraltar faces on the Pacific Ocean?

Answer on page 10, Blue Section

(33)

Catch On?

QUIZ 5. What two letters, coming in alphabetical order, spell a word? The same two letters turned around spell another word. What are the two words?

Answer on page 10, Blue Section

Presidential Names

QUIZ 6. Five of our Presidents had the first name of James. How many of our Presidents had last names ending in "son"? Score 10 points for naming 3.

Answer on page 11, Blue Section

Auntie's Age

QUIZ 7. What would be the age of your aunt if she told you that she was married at 23 and that if she lived 23 more years she would be married 60 years?

Answer on page 11, Blue Section

On the Down Beat?

QUIZ 8. Even though the score of a piece of music were particularly difficult, how could you immediately distinguish the half notes from the quarter notes when trying to read it?

Answer on page 11, Blue Section

Making Calls

QUIZ 9. What countries would you have had to visit in order to pay a call on:

        (a) the Maid of Orleans
        (b) the Blind Beggarman
        (c) the Mad Monk

Score 10 points for 2 out of 3.

Answer on page 11, Blue Section

This Is Tricky!

QUIZ 10. If we took you for a ride on a streetcar, and we saw a Civil War veteran on the same car, what would you call him?

Answer on page 11, Blue Section

WHO, WHAT, WHERE, WHEN AND WHICH

1. Was slavery abolished first in the British Empire or in the United States?
2. Whose portrait appears on the one dollar bill?
3. What device did the Greeks use to gain entry into the city of Troy?
4. Is a cat-o'-nine-tails a freak feline?
5. What name is sometimes given to the first ten amendments of the Constitution of the United States?
6. In whose Presidential campaign was the slogan "Tippecanoe and Tyler too" used?
7. What queen ruled a country for more than sixty years?
8. Name the one mammal that is able to fly.
9. Where in the United States does the flag wave day and night?
10. When is a horse not a horse?
11. Recite the first three letters of the alphabet in the Morse Code.
12. Which is the "hot corner" of a baseball diamond?
13. Who lived at 221 B Baker Street?
14. How many squares are there on a checker board?
15. A right angle is what part of a straight angle?
16. What is a dogwatch?
17. What one thing did Homer and Milton have in common besides poetry?
18. What sport is headlined at the first of each year?
19. Between what two cities was the first telegraph message sent?
20. Which side of the Indian's face is seen on the nickel?
21. What part of a calendar is reminiscent of an edible fruit?
22. What "quiz" is conducted over the entire United States once every ten years?
23. What relation was Napoleon III to Napoleon I?
24. What instrument is used to give pitch in a symphony orchestra?

Answers on pages 11 and 12, Blue Section

QUIZ KIDS

POPULAR QUIZ—NUMBER FIFTEEN

Get the "Wright" Answer

QUIZ 1. We hope you will get this one right. In what field did these Wrights gain fame?

      (a) Harold Bell Wright
      (b) Orville Wright
      (c) Sir Almroth Edward Wright

Score 10 points for 2 out of 3.

Answer on page 12, Blue Section

What Relation?

QUIZ 2. George Washington is known as "the Father of his Country." What relation was he to John and Martha Parke Custis?

Answer on page 12, Blue Section

Bend Over!

QUIZ 3. If you were visiting a cave, would you be more apt to bump your head on a stalactite or a stalagmite?

Answer on page 12, Blue Section

Give This the Once-over!

QUIZ 4. Give a slang expression to indicate:

      (a) an acknowledgment of defeat
      (b) to take the consequences
      (c) to buy on credit

Answer on page 12, Blue Section

It Has Teeth in It!

QUIZ 5. What farm implement might be of special interest to a dentist?

Answer on page 12, Blue Section

Money Matters

QUIZ 6. What war saw the introduction of Liberty Loans?

Answer on page 12, Blue Section

Zoological Tools!

QUIZ 7. Distinguish between the alligator wrench and a monkey wrench.

Answer on page 12, Blue Section

Boots and Shoes!

QUIZ 8. Name a type of footgear prominent in connection with each of the following:
- (a) Puss in ———
- (b) Cinderella
- (c) Mercury

Answer on page 12, Blue Section

Give a General Answer

QUIZ 9. The message "From the oldest general in Europe to the greatest general in the world" accompanied a portrait of whom to whom?

Answer on page 12, Blue Section

Cock Robin

QUIZ 10. In the nursery rhyme "Cock Robin," who saw him die; who was the parson; who sang the psalm?
Score 10 points for 2 out of 3.

Answer on page 12, Blue Section

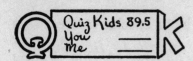

QUIZ KIDS

Take a Collection!

QUIZ 1. What would you have if you were to make a collection of the articles held by:

      (a) Maud Muller
      (b) Little Red Riding Hood
      (c) Justice

Answer on page 12, Blue Section

Name the State

QUIZ 2. What State is round at both ends and high in the middle?

Answer on page 12, Blue Section

A Raphael Painting

QUIZ 3. Raphael painted a picture showing the patron saint of England slaying a dragon. Who is the saint?

Answer on page 12, Blue Section

Get to the Core!

QUIZ 4. A variety of apple can be identified by each of the following descriptions:

      (a) a Biblical character
      (b) an English statesman
      (c) an Arctic undercover agent

Answer on page 13, Blue Section

Things in Common

QUIZ 5. What do fingerprints and snowflakes have in common?

Answer on page 13, Blue Section

Oh, Prunes!

QUIZ 6.   Could you prune a prune tree?

Answer on page 13, Blue Section

Popular Expressions

QUIZ 7.   Give popular expressions containing an author's name that will describe these:

        (a) anger
        (b) surprise
        (c) annoyance

Answer on page 13, Blue Section

Poetic Situations

QUIZ 8.   These situations were taken from what well-known poetry?   What happened when:

        (a) a famous old gentleman placed his finger at the side of his nose
        (b) a little boy wouldn't say his prayers

Answer on page 13, Blue Section

Bowl This One Over!

QUIZ 9.   We all think of Pasadena, California, when the Rose Bowl is mentioned.   What cities do you think of when you hear of these bowls:

        (a) Orange
        (b) Sugar
        (c) Cotton

Answer on page 13, Blue Section

Yes, Vegetables!

QUIZ 10.   What vegetables in your garden would remind you of:

        (a) a result of tight shoes
        (b) a product of a chicken
        (c) a policeman's route

Answer on page 13, Blue Section

QUIZ KIDS

POPULAR QUIZ—NUMBER SEVENTEEN

A Square Question

QUIZ 1. We think this is a square question. In what city is:
- (a) Red Square
- (b) Trafalgar Square
- (c) Independence Square

Score 10 points for 2 out of 3.

Answer on page 13, Blue Section

Get This 1 2!

QUIZ 2. Numerically speaking, what number would indicate:
- (a) the completion of a meal
- (b) a victory
- (c) also

Answer on page 13, Blue Section

Author-Playwrights

QUIZ 3. Name at least two authors that have recently appeared in plays of their own.

Answer on page 13, Blue Section

Birds

QUIZ 4. To what bird would you refer were you to say:
- (a) a mimic winging through the woods
- (b) it's like a rooster's voice
- (c) he's acting like a madman

Score 10 points for 2 out of 3.

Answer on page 13, Blue Section

Coin a Title

QUIZ 5. These popular song titles mention coins. Fill the blanks with the proper coin:

      (a) "Dancing on a ————"

      (b) "Jimmy Had a ————"

      (c) "A ———— for Your Thoughts"

Answer on page 13, Blue Section

Leaders

QUIZ 6. Who were the leaders of the following groups:

      (a) the Green Mountain Boys

      (b) the Rough Riders

Score 5 points for each.

Answer on page 13, Blue Section

Fathers of Many Things

QUIZ 7. Name the following fathers:

      (a) Father of His Country

      (b) Father of the Symphony and Quartet

      (c) Father of Waters

Score 10 points for 2 out of 3.

Answer on page 13, Blue Section

Lead Pencils

QUIZ 8. Lead pencils contain no lead. Do they contain plumbago?

Answer on page 13, Blue Section

Try to Remember!

QUIZ 9. Going back to nursery rhymes, who:

      (a) went to town

      (b) met a pieman

      (c) sat among the cinders

Score 10 points for 2 out of 3.

Answer on page 14, Blue Section

Would It Be Stylish?

QUIZ 10. Could you wear a southwester during a southwester?

Answer on page 14, Blue Section

VARIETY QUIZ

Score

1. Name four of the nine provinces of Canada.................. _____
2. Where is Bedloe Island and why is it famous?.............. _____
3. What is the color of the top light on most traffic signals?.... _____
4. What does a pig boat carry?................................ _____
5. Is Pearl Harbor located in the Pearl Isles?................. _____
6. Name the mountain believed to be the home of the Greek Gods. _____
7. In what famous poem is tintinnabulation found?............ _____
8. In what story did an unpopular ugly bird become a beautiful swan?... _____
9. Name the months in alphabetical order................... _____
10. Under what tree did the village blacksmith stand?.......... _____
11. What was the 48th State and when was it admitted to the Union?... _____
12. Is Barbary Coast a part of the Barbary States?............. _____
13. In what State did the Charter Oak stand?................. _____
14. How many bricks are there in a cement wall 10 feet wide by 10 feet thick?.. _____
15. What was the date of the second inauguration of President Franklin Delano Roosevelt?............................... _____
16. Spell a word that contains all the vowels in their correct order. _____
17. What city is called the "Windy City"?.................... _____
18. Would a restaurant serve bullion as its first course?......... _____
19. Where did the battle of the *Monitor* and the *Merrimac* occur and during which war?................................... _____

Total Score _____

Answers on page 14, Blue Section

QUIZ KIDS

POPULAR QUIZ—NUMBER EIGHTEEN

Quiz Kids 95.7
Yours _____
Mine _____

Try Your Hand at This!

QUIZ 1. In what games are the following terms used:
  (a) meld
  (b) rubber
  (c) checkmate
Score 10 points for 2 out of 3.

Answer on page 14, Blue Section

Watch Your Pennies!

QUIZ 2. What is the difference between a new nickel and an old penny? This is a "catch" question!

Answer on page 15, Blue Section

The Art of Argument

QUIZ 3. If Whistler, Rubens, and Picasso had all lived at the same time, and you found them in a violent argument, what would the subject of discussion probably have been?

Answer on page 15, Blue Section

Now, Let Me See!

QUIZ 4. What was the President's name fifteen years ago?

Answer on page 15, Blue Section

There Oughta Be a Law!

QUIZ 5. In the making of laws, what is the process of referendum?

Answer on page 15, Blue Section

Finders Keepers?

QUIZ 6. The losers were the weepers in the following nursery rhymes. What did each one of them lose?

        (a) "Little Bo-Peep"
        (b) "The Three Little Kittens"

Answer on page 15, Blue Section

Royal Jewels

QUIZ 7. The so-called "King" and "Queen" of all gems are also the most widely worn in imitation jewelry. Which two precious stones are they?

Answer on page 15, Blue Section

Lock the Doors!

QUIZ 8. What is the difference between robbery and burglary?

Answer on page 15, Blue Section

A Seasonable Question

QUIZ 9. Although one of our four seasons may not seem the longest, at least in the northern sections of the country, which is actually the longest?

Answer on page 15, Blue Section

From A to Z

QUIZ 10. If you read through the encyclopedia, your mind would be so cluttered with facts that you would probably have to stop before you came to the letter "Z." But you might have started your reading backwards, in which case you would be able to identify at least two of the following items that begin with the letter "Z." What are they?

        (a) an animal
        (b) a French novelist
        (c) a dirigible

Answer on page 15, Blue Section

1.

2.

3.

4.

OUT OF THE PAGES OF BOOKS

Here are four little children whose names are the same as the
stories from which they come. Name the four stories.

Answer on page 31, Blue Section

QUIZ KIDS

POPULAR QUIZ—NUMBER NINETEEN

Sing a Song

QUIZ 1. What coin are we asked to sing about in the nursery rhyme that includes "blackbirds baked in a pie"?

Answer on page 15, Blue Section

A Coat of Many Colors

QUIZ 2. A coat of many colors, which would probably be called a "blazer" today, was involved in the story concerning what father and which of his twelve sons?

Answer on page 15, Blue Section

English Queens

QUIZ 3. Two of the most important eras in English history were named after the queens ruling during these periods. What queens were they?

Score 5 points for each.

Answer on page 15, Blue Section

Refrigeration

QUIZ 4. We think of the use of a refrigerator in connection with keeping foodstuffs cold, thereby preserving them. To what use could one put a refrigerator in sub-zero weather?

Answer on page 15, Blue Section

Holidays

QUIZ 5. Christmas always falls on December 25th; Independence Day on July 4th. On what date does Easter fall?

Answer on page 15, Blue Section

Escape!

QUIZ 6. A prisoner is locked in a tower room 50 feet from the ground with no way of escape except by means of a rope. He has a very stout rope, but it is only 25 feet long. How can he reach the ground by using the rope?

Answer on page 15, Blue Section

Legs or Tail?

QUIZ 7. What animal is an excellent example of evolution in that it is born with a tail and no legs, and ends its life with legs and no tail?

Answer on page 15, Blue Section

Land of Lakes

QUIZ 8. What State, whose fictional history features the story of Paul Bunyan creating its lakes, is called the "Lake State," due to its many thousands of lakes?

Answer on page 15, Blue Section

Automobiles

QUIZ 9. You are familiar with many makes of automobiles. Name at least three now being produced that are named after their manufacturers.

Answer on page 15, Blue Section

A President

QUIZ 10. Who was the first war-time President of the United States?

Answer on page 15, Blue Section

(47)

QUIZ KIDS

POPULAR QUIZ—NUMBER TWENTY

She Knew Paris

QUIZ 1. We cannot believe that the woman about whom the following lines were written was any more beautiful than many of our movie stars. However, her beauty was immortalized in legend and poetry. Who was she?

"Was this the face that launched a thousand ships,
And burnt the topless towers of Ilium——"

Answer on page 16, Blue Section

A Matter of Dressing

QUIZ 2. Name two things, other than babies, that are "dressed."

Answer on page 16, Blue Section

Age Will Out!

QUIZ 3. We don't exactly know what age has to do with history, but for the sake of information, which of the following is the oldest and which the youngest:
- (a) Hitler
- (b) Mussolini
- (c) King George VI
- (d) President Roosevelt

Answer on page 16, Blue Section

A Question of Sleep

QUIZ 4. Perhaps you are lucky enough to be able to say of yourself that you "sleep like a top." What is the source of the expression?

Answer on page 16, Blue Section

(48)

Familiar Paintings

QUIZ 5. Fill in the blank in the title of each of the following famous paintings:

      (a) *The Last* ———————

      (b) *The Girl with a* ———————

      (c) *The* ——— *Madonna*

Score 10 points for 2 out of 3.

Answer on page 16, Blue Section

Vegetable Seeds

QUIZ 6. The edible part of some vegetables is the stalk, of others the leaves, and of still others the root. Name three vegetables of which we eat only the seeds.

Answer on page 16, Blue Section

The Front of a Box Car?

QUIZ 7. You have probably been stopped at railroad crossings to wait for long strings of box cars to go by. Which is the front end of a box car?

Answer on page 16, Blue Section

Less Noise?

QUIZ 8. If you were playing a musical instrument and read in the music the term "decrescendo," would you gradually decrease your tone volume or the time of the music?

Answer on page 16, Blue Section

It's not a Broom!

QUIZ 9. The following couplet describes a means of transportation. What is it?

        A whirring sound and off it flies
        To sweep the cobwebs from the skies.

Answer on page 16, Blue Section

Don't Moon over This

QUIZ 10. What is between the earth and the sun during a solar eclipse?

Answer on page 16, Blue Section

FILL-IN QUIZ

1. The Mardi Gras is held at _____ .
2. The State of Florida is bordered by the States _____ and _____ .
3. A boat sailing down the Mississippi is going in a _____ direction.
4. President Andrew Jackson of the United States was known as "_____ ."
5. A _____ horse, a _____ horse, and a _____ horse do not eat hay.
6. _____ , _____ , and _____ are athletic contests in which it is necessary to go backwards to win.
7. The three kings who occupied the throne of England at various times during one year were _____ , _____ , and _____ .
8. The flag that flew at Washington's inauguration had _____ stars arranged in a _____ .
9. One who analyzes is an _____ . A historian is an _____ .
10. The "reel" is a dance often associated with the State of _____ .
11. _____ and _____ fought a famous duel in the early days of the United States.
12. The council called by Charles V in 1521 to try Martin Luther was called the _____ .
13. The battleship *Maine* was sunk at _____ Harbor in the year _____ .
14. _____ , a famous American movie comedian, was once a British music-hall performer.
15. A person who customarily ate huge quantities of very ordinary food would be called a _____ .
16. _____ University was established by the Massachusetts Bay Colony.
17. Walt Whitman refers to _____ in his poem "O Captain! My Captain!"
18. The Battle of Bunker Hill was won by the _____ .
19. The imaginary belt which encircles the heavens and which is divided into twelve parts is called the _____ .

Answers on pages 16 and 17, Blue Section

QUIZ KiDS

Quiz Kids   93
Yours ____
Mine   ____

Pitch into This One!

QUIZ 1. If you were said to possess absolute pitch, would it mean that you would be a find for the baseball leagues?

Answer on page 17, Blue Section

Famous First Lines

QUIZ 2. These are opening lines of famous books. Identify them.

(a) "My father had a small estate in Nottingham-shire."

(b) "I was born in the year 1632 in the city of York."

(c) "Whoever has made a voyage up the Hudson must remember the Kaatskill Mountains."

Score 10 points for 2 out of 3.

Answer on page 17, Blue Section

A Material Question

QUIZ 3. What materials would you use in:

(a) splicing
(b) welding
(c) dovetailing

Score 10 points for 2 out of 3.

Answer on page 17, Blue Section

Sheep Appetites

QUIZ 4. Why do white sheep eat more than black sheep?

Answer on page 17, Blue Section

Walks

QUIZ 5. Your dancing partner has asked, "May I have the next walk with you?" Name two dances that you might do.

Answer on page 17, Blue Section

Heavens!

QUIZ 6. If you were asked to make a drawing of a haddock in a hammock on a hummock under a hemlock, what would your picture contain?

Score 10 points for 2.

Answer on page 17, Blue Section

Sail Through This One!

QUIZ 7. Who might sing a ditty while using a ditty box?

Answer on page 17, Blue Section

A Census of Censors?

QUIZ 8. Is the census board the same as a board of censors?

Answer on page 17, Blue Section

Twin Cities

QUIZ 9. St. Paul and Minneapolis are often called the "Twin Cities." What might be the twin of these:

    (a) Kansas City, Kansas
    (b) Duluth, Minnesota
    (c) San Francisco, California

Answer on page 17, Blue Section

A Pearly Question

QUIZ 10. Could you have "The Pearl of the Antilles" made into a ring?

Answer on page 17, Blue Section

QUIZ KIDS

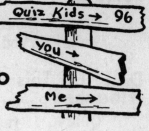

POPULAR QUIZ—NUMBER TWENTY-TWO

Two Left Feet?

QUIZ 1. When you are shopping for shoes, you want both feet to be shod alike. One exception to this rule is when you are buying shoes for a certain popular sport. What sport is it?

Answer on page 17, Blue Section

Try This, Boy, and See!

QUIZ 2. What name is given to the uplifting force of liquids upon immersed objects?

Answer on page 17, Blue Section

One Isn't a Hat!

QUIZ 3. Brown derbies are not so popular as black ones, but there are two exceptions. One was made famous by a former governor of New York, the other is found in California. Identify them further.

Answer on page 17, Blue Section

Five? One? Ten? Twenty?

QUIZ 4. For how many years less than a century does the United States' lease of air and naval bases run?

Answer on page 17, Blue Section

A Little . . . . Miss

QUIZ 5. Heidi is a famous little girl of fiction. With what country is she identified?

Answer on page 17, Blue Section

Personal History

QUIZ 6. Is it correct to call the story that you would write about your own life a biography?

Answer on page 17, Blue Section

Don't Let This One Tree You!

QUIZ 7. Place the name of trees in the following sentences:
    (a) He held a marble in the ——— of his hand.
    (b) She bought an expensive ——— coat.

Answer on page 18, Blue Section

This One Has a Foundation

QUIZ 8. If your conversation were sprinkled with terms such as rafters, studs, and joists, what would you probably be discussing?

Answer on page 18, Blue Section

A Tropical Short

QUIZ 9. If you went to a movie and saw a short about Bali or Bermuda, how would you classify the short?

Answer on page 18, Blue Section

Can You Map Out an Answer?

QUIZ 10. If you were a cartographer, what would be your work?

Answer on page 18, Blue Section

QUIZZICAL QUIZ NUMBER FIVE

You are in the bathroom taking a bath. Accidentally you break the handle off the faucet and you are unable to turn the water off. The door is locked from the outside and there is no one else in the house. The only other outlet in the room is a small aperture near the ceiling for ventilation. How would you save yourself from drowning? Remember, you can't turn the water off!

Answer on page 31, Blue Section

QUIZ KIDS

POPULAR QUIZ—NUMBER TWENTY-THREE

Four Little Letters!

QUIZ 1. The letters of a four-letter word meaning a small particle can be rearranged and defined as below. What is the word? What is the word as defined in each of the following:

(a) a separate piece of news
(b) to send forth
(c) a reckoning of duration

Score 10 points for 2 out of 3.

Answer on page 18, Blue Section

Don't Run from This Question!

QUIZ 2. If you keep track of sports, you will know what sport to associate with the names Munski and Fenske. What is it?

Answer on page 18, Blue Section

Colorful Mountain Names

QUIZ 3. Four of the mountain ranges making up the Appalachian Mountains have the names of colors. What are they?

Answer on page 18, Blue Section

Musical Fathers

QUIZ 4. Who are the following eighteenth century fathers who are often referred to as:

(a) the Father of Modern Music
(b) the Father of Modern Opera

Score 5 points for each.

Answer on page 18, Blue Section

(55)

He Wrote "The Raven"

QUIZ 5. What river in Italy would remind you of a famous poet and story writer? Who was he?

Answer on page 18, Blue Section

A Simple Question

QUIZ 6. If you were a lawyer and wished to do a man a favor by charging a small fee for your services, would you say you were charging a simple fee or a fee simple?

Answer on page 18, Blue Section

Names in the Alphabet

QUIZ 7. What letters of the alphabet would identify:
- (a) an American statesman
- (b) a movie actress
- (c) a novel by Mary Roberts Rinehart

Score 10 points for 2 out of 3.

Answer on page 18, Blue Section

Don't Go Away Mad!

QUIZ 8. Why is the letter "D" like a cross baby?

Answer on page 18, Blue Section

Multiplication and Subtraction

QUIZ 9. What is the difference between twice eight and twenty and twice twenty-eight?

Answer on page 18, Blue Section

Sing This Answer!

QUIZ 10. What might be a theme song for these parties:
- (a) a barnyard party
- (b) a hard-times party
- (c) a baby party

Answer on page 18, Blue Section

QUIZ KIDS

POPULAR QUIZ—NUMBER TWENTY-FOUR

Testing Temperature

QUIZ 1. There are more ways than one of measuring heat and cold. In fact, you may have a triple check. What are the three scales for telling temperature?

Score 10 points for 2 out of 3.

Answer on page 18, Blue Section

Boys Will Be Boys!

QUIZ 2. Speaking of boys, define:
        (a) a hautboy
        (b) a bus boy
        (c) a doughboy

Score 10 points for 2 out of 3.

Answer on page 18, Blue Section

He Wore a Blue Suit

QUIZ 3. A painting by Thomas Gainsborough, a nursery rhyme, and a famous poem by Eugene Field were composed about boys in blue. Identify them.

Answer on page 18, Blue Section

Colorful Feelings

QUIZ 4. Certain emotions are associated with colors. For example, we say, "purple with rage." Now suppose the color of cowardice were mixed with the color of unhappiness, what color and what emotion would result?

Score 5 points for each part.

Answer on page 19, Blue Section

(57)

What, No Cuff?

Quiz 5. Don't get into a huff and muff this answer in trying to determine what games or sports use the following terms. What are they?

        (a) luff
        (b) ruff
        (c) buff

Score 10 points for 2 out of 3.

Answer on page 19, Blue Section

Can You Talk Turkey?

Quiz 6. You needn't be cosmopolitan to give the meaning of the following terms. What are they?

        (a) French leave
        (b) Indian giver
        (c) Chinaman's chance

Answer on page 19, Blue Section

Get Out Your Checkbook

Quiz 7. If you could bring yourself to write out a check for eleven thousand, eleven hundred, eleven dollars, how would you write it?

Answer on page 19, Blue Section

Confucius Ask!

Quiz 8. "Confucius Say" became a fad in the United States, but what is Confucianism?

Answer on page 19, Blue Section

Try This One on Your Feet!

Quiz 9. If you walked half the width of your dining room, then walked half the width of the space between you and the opposite wall, then half the quarter nearest the wall, then half the remaining space, and so on, would you finally reach the wall? Theoretically? Practically?

Answer on page 19, Blue Section

Speechless!

QUIZ 10. What invention, put on a commercial basis by an Italian inventor, is described in the following couplet:

> A messenger that's never seen,
> Yet carries news, the lands between.

Answer on page 19, Blue Section

FIGURE FUN

1. Multiply the number of "Little Pigs" by the number of "Snow White's Dwarfs" and add the number of "Horsemen of the Apocalypse," and state the answer.

2. A man wished to give a group of small boys 5¢ each, but found that he lacked 6¢. He gave them 3¢ each and had 4¢ left. How many boys were there, and how much money did the man have?

3. Divide the number of the year Columbus discovered America by half the number of men in a football backfield and add the digits. Your answer is the title of a novel by what famous American author?

4. If you made an investment of $500 and were given your choice of a 6% dividend at the end of one year, or a dividend of ½ of 1% a month for a period of one year to be paid at the end of the twelfth month, which would you choose?

5. A man bought a horse for $70, sold him for $80, bought him back for $90, and again sold him for $100. Did he make money, lose, or break even on the deal?

6. If your big-toes were thumbs and your little toes were fingers and your fingers were all thumbs, how many more of one kind would you have than of the other?

7. If you see a group of children walking down the road in single file and there are two before two, two between two, and two behind two, how many children are there in the group?

8. A snail climbs a ten-foot pole. Each day he climbs up four feet and each night he slips back two feet. How many days does it take him to reach the top of the pole?

9. A cow was in a field of 1000 acres. She was tied to a rope 20 feet long. Over what area could she graze?

Answers on page 19, Blue Section

ANIMALS FROM STORYLAND

The animals in these pictures have come right from storyland.
It is your problem to name the six stories they represent.

Answer on page 31, Blue Section

Quiz Kids

POPULAR QUIZ—NUMBER TWENTY-FIVE

Named After Tribes

QUIZ 1. There are at least three States that have the same name as Indian tribes. Name two.

Answer on page 19, Blue Section

Battle Boundaries

QUIZ 2. Within the boundaries of what countries would you have been stationed had you participated in:

  (a) the Battle of Waterloo
  (b) the Battle of Bannockburn
  (c) the Battle of Corunna

Score 10 points for 2 out of 3.

Answer on page 19, Blue Section

No Squareheads?

QUIZ 3. You've heard people called "blockheads," but who were the "Roundheads"?

Answer on page 20, Blue Section

Reminders

QUIZ 4. These descriptions should remind you of the names of what famous authors:

  (a) a small thorny tree
  (b) part of a hospital
  (c) a kind of head covering

Answer on page 20, Blue Section

(61)

Get Half of These!

QUIZ 5. Tennessee is bounded by eight States. Name four of them.

Answer on page 20, Blue Section

A Queer Nut

QUIZ 6. A member of the nut family is shaped like a comma and sounds like a sneeze. What is it?

Answer on page 20, Blue Section

The "Eyes" Have It!

QUIZ 7. What is the difference between an ordinary sewing needle and the needle of a sewing machine?

Answer on page 20, Blue Section

Ghosts!

QUIZ 8. Is a ghost in a television studio a script writer?

Answer on page 20, Blue Section

Streets

QUIZ 9. What characters, real or from books, would you be likely to meet in:
- (a) Wimpole Street
- (b) Quality Street
- (c) Main Street

Answer on page 20, Blue Section

Three Farm Animals

QUIZ 10. If Reynard is a name for a fox, what animal is called:
- (a) Bossy
- (b) Tabby
- (c) Dobbin

Answer on page 20, Blue Section

QUIZ KIDS

POPULAR QUIZ—NUMBER TWENTY-SIX

Everything!

QUIZ 1. What did Benjamin Disraeli and the Earl of Beaconsfield have in common?

Answer on page 20, Blue Section

A Question of Love

QUIZ 2. By whom were the following loved, as commemorated by song and story:

        (a) Cleopatra
        (b) Queen of Sheba
        (c) Queen in Calico

Answer on page 20, Blue Section

Men in Songs

QUIZ 3. Name at least two songs that contain both the first and last names of a man in their titles.

Answer on page 20, Blue Section

They Are Different!

QUIZ 4. Although they sound very similar, chain mail and chain letters differ extremely. What is the difference?

Answer on page 20, Blue Section

How Many People?

QUIZ 5. Nevada has the smallest population of any State in the Union. Name three States with the largest populations.

Answer on page 20, Blue Section

Aren't You Curious?

QUIZ 6. A quicker way to say all this will be found in a four-word proverb: Habitual anxiety for information concerning the affairs of others dispatched a well-known domesticated animal. What is the proverb?

Answer on page 20, Blue Section

Try It!

QUIZ 7. If you were to put ten books, each of which was one inch wide, on a shelf in your library, what would they measure from the first page of the first book to the last page of the last book?

Answer on page 20, Blue Section

It's not Sherlock Holmes!

QUIZ 8. What famous fictional detective has his father's fullest co-operation in crime solving, due to the latter gentleman's being a police inspector?

Answer on page 21, Blue Section

Five Pronouns

QUIZ 9. Name a five-letter word which contains five pronouns. The first is simply the letter "u"; the others are spelled correctly.

Answer on page 21, Blue Section

Calico

QUIZ 10. Eugene Field, the poet, wrote about the gingham dog and the calico cat. Were they any relation to a calico horse?

Answer on page 21, Blue Section

QUIZZICAL QUIZ NUMBER SIX

Is it correct to say "the yolk of an egg is white," or "the yolk of an egg are white"?

Answer on page 31, Blue Section

QUIZ KIDS

POPULAR QUIZ — NUMBER TWENTY-SEVEN

Quiz Kids 86.8
Yours ____
Mine ✓

Title in Numbers

QUIZ 1. Two book titles when added would total 1936. One book was written by Booth Tarkington, the other by John Dos Passos. What are the books?

Score 5 points for each.

Answer on page 21, Blue Section

In What State?

QUIZ 2. In what State would you be, if you wandered through Death Valley?

Answer on page 21, Blue Section

Three to Tea

QUIZ 3. Imagine you were having tea with Richard Brimsley Sheridan, Charles Reade, and Arnold Bennett. What might your conversation be about?

Answer on page 21, Blue Section

Kitty, Kitty, Kitty!

QUIZ 4. Give the authors of:
- (a) *Kitty Foyle*
- (b) *Kitty*
- (c) *Kitty Canary*

Score 10 points for 2 out of 3.

Answer on page 21, Blue Section

Mother Goose Puzzler

QUIZ 5. According to Mother Goose, what is "like a garden full of weeds"?

Answer on page 21, Blue Section

Jacks-of-All-Trades!

QUIZ 6. What famous American naturalist was also an artist, and what American minister to France was also a writer and famous scientist?

Score 5 points for each.

Answer on page 21, Blue Section

Well, Hardly!

QUIZ 7. We're supposed to be happy when we sing, but should you be happy if you were in Sing Sing?

Answer on page 21, Blue Section

Bad Conversation

QUIZ 8. If your conversation is of malversation, what are you discussing?

Answer on page 21, Blue Section

Fighting Names!

QUIZ 9. Supply the last names of these fighters:
- (a) Tony
- (b) Arturo
- (c) Lou

Score 10 points for 2 out of 3.

Answer on page 21, Blue Section

Our Northernmost State

QUIZ 10. Which State of the United States is nearest the North Pole?

Answer on page 21, Blue Section

QUIZ KIDS

POPULAR QUIZ—NUMBER TWENTY-EIGHT

A? E? I? O? U?

QUIZ 1. One of the vowels does not begin the name of any one of our States. Which is it?

Answer on page 21, Blue Section

The Name Is Victor

QUIZ 2. "To the victor belong the spoils," but it won't spoil your score if you get only two of these Victors! Name them.

(a) a famous novelist
(b) a composer and conductor
(c) a present-day monarch

Score 10 points for 2 out of 3.

Answer on page 21, Blue Section

Sight-seeing

QUIZ 3. Where would you have been visiting if you had been:

(a) looking at the most famous rock in the United States
(b) watching the mist rising along the horseshoe
(c) touring the upper peninsula

Answer on page 21, Blue Section

Be Careful!

QUIZ 4. If there are twelve three-cent stamps in a dozen, how many two-cent stamps are there?

Answer on page 21, Blue Section

(67)

A Question of Length

QUIZ 5. Which is longer, a pole, a perch, or a rod?

Answer on page 21, Blue Section

A Riddle to Egg You On!

QUIZ 6. Crack this riddle:

> As I was walking thro' a field of rye,
> I picked up something we often buy.
> 'Twas neither bone nor meat
> Yet it grew to have a beak.

Answer on page 21, Blue Section

Small Change!

QUIZ 7. A man owes you a note amounting to two thousand dollars. The day the note is due, he comes to your office and says he is prepared to pay the note but finds he must pay it in specie. How does he pay the note—by check, bank notes, coin, bank draft, or United States money order?

Answer on page 21, Blue Section

This Sounds Mournful!

QUIZ 8. What is a monody?

Answer on page 21, Blue Section

Song Titles

QUIZ 9. If you sang the following words, what songs should you be singing:

> (a) "Darling, I am growing old."
> (b) "I'd give the world to live again the lovely past."
> (c) "Once I was happy, but now I'm forlorn."

Score 10 points for 2 out of 3.

Answer on page 22, Blue Section

"Name" Products

QUIZ 10. Colt, Otis, Goodyear, and Bell were all inventors. Each had a product, which is still in use, named after him. Name the products.

Score 10 points for 2 out of 3.

Answer on page 22, Blue Section

TWO'S AND THREE'S

1. Name two of the best-known "lake poets."
2. Name three birds whose call is the same as their names.
3. Name two artists that are identified as "Impressionists."
4. Name three world-famed personalities that never lived.
5. Name two of the three ships in the fleet of Christopher Columbus on his first voyage.
6. Name two things other than yarn that can be knitted.
7. Name three articles for eating that are mentioned in the nursery rhymes.
8. Name three of the five States whose capitals begin with the letter "A."
9. Name two personages of ancient times that are used as models of perfect friendship.
10. Name three different things identified by the word "chiffon."
11. Name two ways a baseball player can get to first base other than by a safe hit.
12. Name three occupations ending in "smith."
13. Name three gaits a five-gaited horse has besides a walk.
14. Name two of the three United States Presidents that died on July 4th.
15. Name three different ways in which the word "belt" may be used.
16. Name the three animals mentioned in the song, "Home on the Range."
17. Name three famous German composers whose last names begin with the letter "B."
18. Name two of the three State capitals that lie on the banks of the Missouri River.
19. Name three species of fruit, one which rhymes with a place of worship, one which rhymes with a sandy shore, and one which rhymes with the first digit of the hand. Example: What fruit rhymes with a female horse? Pear (mare).

Answers on page 22, Blue Section

QUIZ KIDS

POPULAR QUIZ—NUMBER TWENTY-NINE

Throw a Little Light on This One!

QUIZ 1. We believe you will first think of a city when you read this one. Identify:

      (a) Aurora Rosyfinger

      (b) aurora borealis

      (c) aurora australis

Answer on page 22, Blue Section

He Said, "I Do"!

QUIZ 2. In Shakespeare's *Much Ado About Nothing* when did Benedick become a benedict? Why?

Answer on page 23, Blue Section

National Drinks

QUIZ 3. If you were wining with three men and were to guess their native lands from their orders, how should you identify one who ordered:

      (a) vodka

      (b) sake

      (c) mescal

Score 10 points for 2 out of 3.

Answer on page 23, Blue Section

Oh, Doctor!

QUIZ 4. If your doctor said you lacked red corpuscles, should you be suffering from anemia or amnesia?

Answer on page 23, Blue Section

A King's Grandson

QUIZ 5. What American statesman was the grandson of a king?

Answer on page 23, Blue Section

A Three-Term Job

QUIZ 6. James Wilson had the distinction of having served as Secretary of Agriculture under three Presidents. Who were they?

Answer on page 23, Blue Section

High Finance

QUIZ 7. If you have $1.15 in six coins and are unable to change either a dollar, a half dollar, a quarter, a dime, or a nickel, what coins do you have?

Answer on page 23, Blue Section

What's the Name?

QUIZ 8. A child of the comic strips has the same first name as the famous American author of *Hyperion*. What is the full name of each?

Answer on page 23, Blue Section

A Question of Dogs

QUIZ 9. If you were seeking a good dog for rounding up cattle, would you choose a prairie dog? Why?

Answer on page 23, Blue Section

Dressed Skin

QUIZ 10. Animal skin is sometimes dressed and prepared for writing purposes. What is it called?

Answer on page 23, Blue Section

QUIZZICAL QUIZ NUMBER SEVEN

If your business made you selfish, what would it be?

Answer on page 31, Blue Section

QUIZ KIDS
POPULAR QUIZ—NUMBER THIRTY

Famous Ferdinands

QUIZ 1. We'll leave one Ferdinand with his flowers while you identify these Ferdinands:

      (a) a generalissimo of the Allied Armies in 1918
      (b) a famous engineer
      (c) a great navigator

Answer on page 23, Blue Section

Would You Be Hurt?

QUIZ 2. If you were to say you were "lapidified" by an accident, what should you mean?

Answer on page 23, Blue Section

Scenic Song Suggestions

QUIZ 3. What songs might be suggested by these scenic descriptions:

      (a) "the wide-spreading pond and the mill that stood by it"
      (b) "silver sails all out of the west"
      (c) "the creek and the old rusty mill"

Score 10 points for 2 out of 3.

Answer on page 23, Blue Section

From the New Testament

QUIZ 4. What did the daughter of Jairus, the son of the Widow of Nain, and Lazarus, the brother of Mary and Martha, have in common?

Answer on page 23, Blue Section

Heap-Famous Brave

QUIZ 5. Which of these famous Indians is a fictional character? Whose book made him famous?

    (a) Geronimo
    (b) Uncas
    (c) Sequoyah

Answer on page 23, Blue Section

It Also Causes March Headaches!

QUIZ 6. Which amendment to the Constitution has proved to be the source of greatest revenue for the United States Treasury? Tell why it has been so.

Answer on page 23, Blue Section

Read Carefully!

QUIZ 7. If you bought a ten-cent box of extra long pins what did you buy them for?

Answer on page 23, Blue Section

Alphabetical Addition

QUIZ 8. What two letters when prefixed by the letter "b" become a body of water; by the letter "j," a bird; by the letter "h," a grass?

Score 10 points for 2 out of 3.

Answer on page 23, Blue Section

Central American Geography

QUIZ 9. One Central American country does not touch the Caribbean Sea. Another does not touch the Pacific Ocean. Name the two countries.

Score 5 points for each one.

Answer on page 23, Blue Section

A Question of Letters

QUIZ 10. What three letters appearing in QUIZ KIDS Questions do not appear in any of the names of the months?

Answer on page 23, Blue Section

TRUE OR FALSE

	True or False	Score
1. The ostrich is the largest living bird.		
2. Aristotle went out with a lantern to find an honest man.		
3. If your doctor prescribed insulin, you would be suffering from insomnia.		
4. There are four different groups or types of blood.		
5. The whale is noted for its ability to jump waterfalls.		
6. Twenty-one of our Presidents were lawyers.		
7. Leonardo da Vinci painted *The Gleaners.*		
8. Australia is the largest island in the world.		
9. Monticello is famous as the home of Thomas Jefferson.		
10. There are more girls born each year than there are boys.		
11. Thirty-three years is usually considered a generation.		
12. The flag of the United States of America has six red and seven white stripes.		
13. A hangar belongs in a clothes closet.		
14. A bugbear is an animal.		
15. Charles Dickens wrote *Tale of Two Cities.*		
16. Europe has no desert areas.		
17. A Roman coin dated 105 B.C. would be fraudulent.		
18. A penny covers a larger area than a dime.		
19. A *montage* is an optical illusion.		
20. The word "veto" appears twice in the Constitution of the United States.		

Score 5 points for each answered correctly.   Total Score _____

Answers on pages 23 and 24, Blue Section

THE ABSENT-MINDED ARTIST

The artist who drew this picture was thinking of other things.
List all the mistakes that he has made in the drawing.

Answer on page 32, Blue Section

QUIZ KIDS

POPULAR QUIZ—NUMBER THIRTY-ONE

They Were in Conference

QUIZ 1. At what famous conference did Lloyd George, George Clemenceau, Woodrow Wilson, and Vittorio Orlando meet?

Answer on page 24, Blue Section

A Sweet Question

QUIZ 2. If eight QUIZ KIDS had only seven pieces of candy of equal size, how could they each receive the same amount of candy and still slice each piece only once?

Answer on page 24, Blue Section

One Is not a Tortilla!

QUIZ 3. There are two Mexican dishes with which most Americans are familiar. One begins with the English term for heat and the other sounds like a term for cold. What weather report can you make from them?

Answer on page 24, Blue Section

Watch This Carefully

QUIZ 4. Give the first and last dates of the first year of the 21st century?

Answer on page 24, Blue Section

A Swiss Admiral?

QUIZ 5. Why shouldn't you be flattered if you were offered a high commission in the Swiss Navy?

Answer on page 24, Blue Section

A Biblical Question

QUIZ 6. What is the first sentence in the Bible?

Answer on page 24, Blue Section

This Is a Daisy!

QUIZ 7. "Donald Duck" and "Blondie," comic strips, have characters bearing the same name. Who are they?

Answer on page 24, Blue Section

A Trudgen Would Do!

QUIZ 8. In what sport is the Australian crawl used?

Answer on page 24, Blue Section

A Fueling Question

QUIZ 9. If you were called upon to buy some fuel for heating purposes, what units of measure should you use in buying the following items:

- (a) coal
- (b) wood
- (c) petroleum
- (d) gas

Score 10 points for 3 out of 4.

Answer on page 24, Blue Section

A Very Young Heroine

QUIZ 10. One of Shakespeare's heroines, age thirteen, was extremely sophisticated for her age. Who was she?

Answer on page 24, Blue Section

QUIZ KIDS

POPULAR QUIZ—NUMBER THIRTY-TWO

Don't Peek!

QUIZ 1. Add the numbers on the face of a clock without looking at your watch. What is the sum?

Answer on page 25, Blue Section

Opposites

QUIZ 2. The ends of the following song titles are opposite to the beginnings. Complete them:

(a) "Bitter ———"
(b) "I Forgot to ———"
(c) "Accidently on ———"

Score 10 points for 2 out of 3.

Answer on page 25, Blue Section

The Land of Laps

QUIZ 3. You have heard that Laplanders come from a cold region. Where is Lapland?

Answer on page 25, Blue Section

A Scarlet Question

QUIZ 4. Scarlett O'Hara is a fictional character from *Gone With the Wind* by Margaret Mitchell. Who were the authors of the following Scarlet books:

(a) *A Study in Scarlet*
(b) *The Scarlet Letter*

Score 5 points for each.

Answer on page 25, Blue Section

Stop! Thief!

QUIZ 5. If you were at a baseball game and saw a glaring theft committed, but that theft was loudly applauded by the fans, what might have happened?

Answer on page 25, Blue Section

A Question of Age

QUIZ 6. Many Biblical characters lived longer than do men of the present day. What Biblical character lived the longest of them all?

Answer on page 25, Blue Section

It's not a Game

QUIZ 7. What is the origin and meaning of the expression, "Play Boswell to his Johnson"?

Answer on page 25, Blue Section

A Hat Bears the Same Name

QUIZ 8. Who was the Earl for whom a famous horse race was named? A race of this type is run in England and also in the United States.

Answer on page 25, Blue Section

It's Strong Too!

QUIZ 9. A healthy man and the United States of America have one thing in common. What is it?

Answer on page 25, Blue Section

The Fourth Estate

QUIZ 10. A newspaper is intimately connected with the "fourth estate." Why is this so?

Answer on page 25, Blue Section

QUIZ KIDS

POPULAR QUIZ—NUMBER THIRTY-THREE

Make the Best of This!

QUIZ 1. The fictional character "Pollyanna" created such a strong impression on the minds of the public that the appellation "Pollyanna" was then applied to a certain type of individual. What is its meaning as currently used?

Answer on page 25, Blue Section

Can You Bear This?

QUIZ 2. Children love to cuddle a furry toy that was named after one of our Presidents. What is this toy?

Answer on page 25, Blue Section

Caterpillars

QUIZ 3. A caterpillar is the larva of an insect. What inanimate object is also called a caterpillar?

Answer on page 25, Blue Section

Indian Talk

QUIZ 4. What are the meanings of the following terms adapted from the Indians:
- (a) Happy Hunting Ground
- (b) Powwow
- (c) Bury the Hatchet

Score 10 points for 2 out of 3.

Answer on page 25, Blue Section

Musical Instruments

QUIZ 5. Which of the following instruments does not belong in this grouping?

      (a) Saxophone
      (b) Bugle
      (c) Clarinet
      (d) Oboe

Answer on page 25, Blue Section

Poor Richard

QUIZ 6. *Poor Richard's Almanack* was one of the first books of its kind to be published. Who was its author?

Answer on page 25, Blue Section

A Question of Balance

QUIZ 7. Without our sense of balance, we should have a difficult time standing upright on our two legs. Where is this sense of balance located?

Answer on page 25, Blue Section

Saved!

QUIZ 8. During the War of 1812, the portrait of George Washington was saved from fire by a woman then in the White House. Who was she?

Answer on page 25, Blue Section

It Rhymes with Jail

QUIZ 9. The students and graduates of one of our great universities are referred to as "Sons of Eli." What is the name of the university?

Answer on page 25, Blue Section

Strike This Hard!

QUIZ 10. In what sport do we speak of a "squeeze play"?

Answer on page 26, Blue Section

WHAT QUIZ II

1. What word in the English language beginning with "und" also ends with "und"?
2. What American statesman was referred to as the "Plumed Knight"?
3. What does Flag Day commemorate?
4. What did Caligula have in common with Nero?
5. What body of water did Leander swim in order to see Hero?
6. What is absent-minded scribbling with pencil or pen called?
7. What is the difference between a vivarium and an aquarium?
8. What invention was most responsible for inducting women into the business world?
9. What is a needle valve?
10. What treaty concluded World War I?
11. What do Atlantis, Mu, and Utopia have in common?
12. What do a diamond, the lead in a pencil, and a chunk of coal have in common?
13. What occupation makes use of the terms single-entry and double-entry?
14. What fish could tell a great tale of a man he caught?
15. What three States meet at Cumberland Gap?
16. What does a spendthrift save that a miser spends?
17. What similarity is there in the locations of Albuquerque and El Paso?
18. What is a key signature?
19. What never asks a question yet is always answered?
20. What State has a name that would indicate it was entirely surrounded by water?
21. What do a brogue, a brogan, and a pump have in common?

Answers on page 26, Blue Section

QUIZ KIDS

POPULAR QUIZ—NUMBER THIRTY-FOUR

Not for a One-Track Mind!

QUIZ 1. A train running 40 miles an hour leaves Chicago at 8 o'clock. Another running 60 miles an hour leaves on the same track at 11 o'clock and eventually telescopes the slower train. How far from Chicago did the accident occur? One of the QUIZ KIDS worked this in his head in 12 seconds, but we think you have a right to stick your chest out if you get it before tomorrow's paper comes.

Answer on page 26, Blue Section

Such Grammar!

QUIZ 2. None of us have missed a question in this list. Is anything wrong with that sentence besides its questionable veracity?

Answer on page 26, Blue Section

A Calf's Mother

QUIZ 3. The first letters of the Pacific Coast States name an animal. What is it?

Answer on page 27, Blue Section

An Ill Wind

QUIZ 4. Which of these winds would make housekeeping most difficult:

    (a) a mistral
    (b) a sirocco
    (c) a simoom

Answer on page 27, Blue Section

(83)

Short Entertainment

QUIZ 5. If you were to buy a ticket to see Joseph Barrows, whom should you see, and how should you be entertained?

Answer on page 27, Blue Section

Rock Candy for a Convict?

QUIZ 6. What kind of candy should you appropriately offer:
- (a) a schoolmaster
- (b) a milkman
- (c) a dentist

Answer on page 27, Blue Section

Numbers in the Bible

QUIZ 7. Ten, thirty, and forty have no indication of the score for this list of questions, but these numbers do have Biblical significance. To what do they refer?
Score 10 points for 2 out of 3.

Answer on page 27, Blue Section

My, Such Big Words!

QUIZ 8. Is altruism a synonym or antonym of egoism?

Answer on page 27, Blue Section

There's a Catch to This One!

QUIZ 9. How many apples can you eat on an empty stomach?

Answer on page 27, Blue Section

Food for Mother Hubbard's Cupboard

QUIZ 10. If you were to fill Mother Hubbard's cupboard with food for Curly Locks, Little Miss Muffet, and Jack-a-dandy, what should you place there?

Answer on page 27, Blue Section

QUIZ KIDS

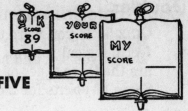

POPULAR QUIZ—NUMBER THIRTY-FIVE

Power Pacts

QUIZ 1. 1922 saw the adoption of the Five-Power Treaties and the Nine-Power Treaties. For what did each provide?
Score 5 points for each.

Answer on page 27, Blue Section

Definitions

QUIZ 2. Identify the units of measurement listed below:

        (a) a dyne

        (b) a lux

        (c) an erg

Score 10 points for 2 out of 3.

Answer on page 27, Blue Section

Verily

QUIZ 3. Have you ever, as you pronounced the word "Amen," stopped to consider its meaning? You know it means "to say or write the last word," but what further meaning does it have?

Answer on page 27, Blue Section

Stars from Abroad

QUIZ 4. Many of our stars of screen and stage come from foreign lands. What are the nationalities of:

        (a) Olivia de Havilland

        (b) Vera Zorina

        (c) Annabella

Score 10 points for 2 out of 3.

Answer on page 27, Blue Section

Doubles

QUIZ 5. If you were to hear of the birth of twins, it would be perfectly logical for you to ask what kind of twins they were. What are the three types of twins?
Score 10 points for 2 out of 3.

Answer on page 27, Blue Section

Will the Suit Fit?

QUIZ 6. If a tailor measured a man for a suit with a tape measure from which the first inch had been cut and then made the suit using a tape measure having the first inch, would the suit fit the customer, be too small, or too large for him?

Answer on page 27, Blue Section

A Matter of Letters

QUIZ 7. What is the similarity found in Alabama and Walla Walla? It has nothing to do with the places, but with the names.

Answer on page 27, Blue Section

Is That All?

QUIZ 8. "I have not yet begun to fight," said a famous American naval officer. Who was he?

Answer on page 27, Blue Section

A Question of Ways

QUIZ 9. The Milky Way is the starry path in the heavens. Where is the "Great White Way"?

Answer on page 28, Blue Section

A Mild Rebuke

QUIZ 10. What mild rebuke would denote the name of what famous Egyptian Pharaoh?

Answer on page 28, Blue Section

QUIZ KIDS

POPULAR QUIZ — NUMBER THIRTY-SIX

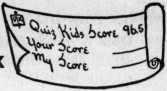

Comparisons

QUIZ 1. If you wished to live a very long time, you might say you should like to be as old as Methuselah. What names might you supply in these wishes:

(a) to be as rich as ———
(b) to be as strong as ———
(c) to be as wise as ———

Answer on page 28, Blue Section

Guess On!

QUIZ 2. Creepers and climbers, runners and scratchers sound like gardening terms, but to what else might these words refer?

Answer on page 28, Blue Section

Fable Titles

QUIZ 3. We don't think you'll score a blank on this one, for we are asking you to supply these blanks in the following fable titles with the name of the right animal:

(a) "The ——— and the Mouse"
(b) "The ——— and the Shadow"
(c) "The ——— and the Grapes"

Answer on page 28, Blue Section

No Home on the Range?

QUIZ 4. What song should you be singing if you sang:

(a) "The birds make music all the day."
(b) "All de world am sad and dreary."
(c) "A charm from the skies seems to hallow us there."

Answer on page 28, Blue Section

(87)

Merry Mix-up

QUIZ 5. Following are two famous quotations that have been scrambled. Unscramble them and assign the spokesman to his quotation: "What I regret is that I know one life, but I read in the papers all I have to lose for my country."

Answer on page 28, Blue Section

Lost Thrones

QUIZ 6. In World War I, at least three of Europe's royal families lost their thrones. Name two.

Answer on page 28, Blue Section

Get Down to Earth!

QUIZ 7. We hope this is in your sphere. Distinguish among:
    (a) hydrosphere
    (b) atmosphere
    (c) lithosphere

Answer on page 28, Blue Section

Work Fast! Grade High!

QUIZ 8. You will have the names of two large foreign cities if you add the syllable "Bel" to the following. Name the cities and their country.
    (a) the word used to denote abstinence from food
    (b) your score on this quiz

Answer on page 28, Blue Section

Three-Alarm Fires

QUIZ 9. What fires do the following dates mark:
    (a) A.D. 64
    (b) 1871
    (c) 1906

Answer on page 28, Blue Section

Don't You Get Trimmed!

QUIZ 10. What would you do if you were:

      (a) to trim a sail

      (b) to trim your neighbor

      (c) to trim a hat

Answer on page 28, Blue Section

WHO, WHAT, WHERE, HOW AND WHY

Score

1. How long does it take the hour hand of a watch to move one minute on the face of the watch? .... _____

2. What word becomes shorter by the addition of one syllable? _____

3. What is a nautical knot? .... _____

4. What city in Texas was named for a one-time governor of Tennessee? .... _____

5. What is a pundit? .... _____

6. Would a cutter with a point of carbon, lead, or steel be used to cut a piece of glass? .... _____

7. What is made from hemp? .... _____

8. What constellation is known as "Lady in Her Chair"? .... _____

9. What wars in England were known by a floral name? .... _____

10. What was the other name of Christ's apostle Simon? .... _____

11. When a bowler scores 300, how many balls does he roll? ...... _____

12. What is the name of the oath to which doctors swear? .... _____

13. If a child went to the butcher shop and asked for a yard of pork, what would he get? .... _____

14. What was the Connecticut Compromise? .... _____

15. How did the term "marathon" originate? .... _____

16. If it were 9 P.M. in your home town, what time would it be at the North Pole? .... _____

17. Why didn't George Eliot live to be an old man? .... _____

18. What do the words "cryptogam" and "cryptogram" mean? .... _____

19. What did Coronado the explorer discover? .... _____

20. How many trips had the *Titanic* made before she sank? ...... _____

Total Score _____

Answers on pages 28 and 29, Blue Section

A "B" HUNT

There are more than twenty-five things in this drawing that begin
with the letter "B." How many of them can you find?

Answer on page 32, Blue Section

QUIZ KIDS

POPULAR QUIZ—NUMBER THIRTY-SEVEN

Distinguished Lees

QUIZ 1. In what wars did these Lees distinguish themselves:

    (a) Henry

    (b) Robert Edward

    (c) Fitzhugh

Score 10 points for 2 out of 3.

Answer on page 29, Blue Section

Oh, Ho!

QUIZ 2. What do you call a word, verse, or sentence that is the same when read backward or forward? Give an example.

Answer on page 29, Blue Section

High Seats

QUIZ 3. What would your title be if you sat upon:

    (a) a throne

    (b) a bench

    (c) a woolsack

Answer on page 29, Blue Section

Wearing Apparel

QUIZ 4. Which of these three things could you wear:

    (a) sharkskin

    (b) net

    (c) duck

Answer on page 29, Blue Section

Inanimate Tongues

QUIZ 5. We all know inanimate objects do not talk, but some do have tongues. Name three.

Answer on page 29, Blue Section

The Faster Walker

QUIZ 6. If Uncle Sam and Mickey Rooney started walking from New York City to Washington, which would arrive first?

Answer on page 29, Blue Section

Mail Initials

QUIZ 7. When the post office receives letters addressed with the following abbreviations, where are they sent?
- (a) P. E. I.
- (b) C. Z.

Answer on page 30, Blue Section

Coolidge's Home State

QUIZ 8. What is the only New England State without a coastline?

Answer on page 30, Blue Section

What About S. C.?

QUIZ 9. The following initials of fictitious people should remind you of Christmas. Who are the people?
- (a) K. K.
- (b) T. T.

Answer on page 30, Blue Section

Watch the Dates

QUIZ 10. When crossing the International Date Line in a westerly direction, i.e., from west longitude to east longitude, is the date advanced one day or set back one day?

Answer on page 30, Blue Section

Quiz Kids

POPULAR QUIZ—NUMBER THIRTY-EIGHT

3-Deckers

QUIZ 1. Your taste may run to 3-decker sandwiches but perhaps you know the author and title of a book that contains 3-decker in its title. Who is he? What is the book?

Answer on page 30, Blue Section

Tons and Tons

QUIZ 2. The short ton is usually used in the United States and Canada, and the long ton is common in Great Britain. What is the difference between them?

Answer on page 30, Blue Section

Take a Shot at This!

QUIZ 3. Perhaps you've been called a blunderbuss when you appeared to be clumsy. What is a blunderbuss?

Answer on page 30, Blue Section

One or the Other Did

QUIZ 4. Did Sherwood Anderson or Thornton Wilder write *Our Town?*

Answer on page 30, Blue Section

High Tide

QUIZ 5. If your boat had a ladder 6 ft. long with 2 ft. of the ladder under water, how much of the ladder would be under water when the tide rises 2 ft.

Answer on page 30, Blue Section

The Eastern Shore

QUIZ 6. You've heard the song "Sailing Down the Chesapeake Bay." If you lived on the eastern shore of Chesapeake Bay, in what State would you reside?

Answer on page 30, Blue Section

Seafood

QUIZ 7. What seafood could you appropriately serve:
- (a) a cross or sulky person
- (b) a person noted for silence
- (c) a puny person

Answer on page 30, Blue Section

Eel Eggs

QUIZ 8. Why is it impossible to find eel eggs in fresh-water lakes and streams?

Answer on page 30, Blue Section

Hawaii

QUIZ 9. Hawaii is the largest of the group composing the Hawaiian Islands. What is the second largest?

Answer on page 30, Blue Section

Varied Professions

QUIZ 10. What professions do you associate with these names:
- (a) Sarah Bernhardt
- (b) J. P. Morgan
- (c) Arthur Sullivan

Score 10 points for 2 out of 3.

Answer on page 30, Blue Section

QUIZZICAL QUIZ NUMBER EIGHT

If you were locked in a room with no possible means of escape, and had with you only a bat and ball, how would you get out?

Answer on page 31, Blue Section

(94)

QUIZ KIDS

POPULAR QUIZ—NUMBER THIRTY-NINE

Quiz Kids Score 91.4
Your Score
My Score

Caves

QUIZ 1. Monument Mountain, Cleveland Avenue, and the Giant Dome are natural features of famous caves. Name the cave to which each belongs.
Score 10 points for 2 out of 3.

Answer on page 30, Blue Section

Such Birds!

QUIZ 2. What bird has the name of:
        (a) a military staff officer
        (b) a machine used for lifting
        (c) a cup or ladle

Answer on page 30, Blue Section

Socrates? Demosthenes?

QUIZ 3. Socrates and Demosthenes are familiar names. Which was an orator and which a philosopher?

Answer on page 30, Blue Section

A Tri-ing Question!

QUIZ 4. How many people would there be if you added to a triple trio a triumvirate and a double quartet?

Answer on page 30, Blue Section

The Prefix Is Different

QUIZ 5. What is the difference between adsorption and absorption?

Answer on page 30, Blue Section

(95)

Song Girls

QUIZ 6. What were the girls' names in the old songs that say:
      (a) " 'Twas not her beauty alone that won me"
      (b) "I'll be waiting at the k-k-k-kitchen door"
      (c) "Sweet personality full of rascality"

Answer on page 31, Blue Section

Slaves

QUIZ 7. History tells us of a slave that became an emperor and of a slave that became a writer of fables. Who were they?

Answer on page 31, Blue Section

How Would You Use It?

QUIZ 8. Should you use an Indian paintbrush to decorate an interior, sweep a floor, or spread on water colors?

Answer on page 31, Blue Section

Watch Out!

QUIZ 9. If sugar is twenty-six cents for five pounds, how much can you buy for a cent and a quarter?

Answer on page 31, Blue Section

Are You Treed?

QUIZ 10. What do laburnum, ironwood, and acacia have in common with a poem by Joyce Kilmer?

Answer on page 31, Blue Section

BLUE SECTION

ANSWERS TO POPULAR QUIZ NUMBER ONE

1. In a book. Flyleaves are the blank leaves at the beginning and end of a book.
2. (a) grove
   (b) orchard
   (c) patch
3. Teaching.
4. Thirty pieces of silver.
5. Baby carriage.
6. Eardrum (drum), heart (pump), and vocal organ (voice box).
7. Sterling silver is an alloy containing a high percentage of silver and a small amount of copper. Silver plate is a material coated or covered with silver.
8. 6-love.
9. A dollar bill.
10. Their hair. Medusa was a Gorgon whose hair had been transformed into snakes. Samson was an Israelite whose great strength was lost when his hair was cut.

ANSWERS TO POPULAR QUIZ NUMBER TWO

1. Louella Parsons writes a syndicated column on Hollywood.
   Luella Gear is a stage personality.
2. (a) tom-tom
   (b) murmur
   (c) hula-hula
3. The "Follies" is a form of musical revue, distinguished by its many beautiful show girls. Flo Ziegfeld was a producer of such revues.
   "Seward's Folly" was the purchase of Alaska from Russia in 1867 for $7,200,000 in gold.
4. All three are American authors.
5. Roughly, the thousand years from the fifth to the fifteenth century after Christ (400—1400 A.D.).

(1)

6. Splash, crack, bowwow, blub, hiss, buzz, and bobwhite. Any others you name may be counted.

7. Ten times. Remember that when the minute hand starts at noon, it does not pass the hour hand, and that at midnight the minute hand is even with, and has not yet passed the hour hand.

8. China, India, and Russia.

9. Orion could drink milk from the Milky Way and use the Big Dipper or the Little Dipper.

10. Yes. Use a penny post card.

ANSWERS TO POPULAR QUIZ NUMBER THREE

1. (a) The refuge for boys established by Father Flanagan. It is also the name of a motion picture starring Spencer Tracy.
   (b) The name of a radio program.
   (c) A motion picture starring Claudette Colbert, Spencer Tracy, Clark Gable, and Hedy Lamarr.

2. Crocodile (crocodile tears).

3. They are both the same distance from New York when they pass each other.

4. King Midas. His food and drink turned into gold at his touch, and he almost starved to death. When his daughter was turned into gold, he asked that the gift be taken away.

5. (a) Joe Kennedy (Joseph P.)
   (b) Joe Di Maggio
   (c) Joe Palooka

6. The organ and the accordion.

7. Dialogue is a conversation in which two or more take part, or a written composition representing two or more persons as conversing or reasoning. Dialect is a language as modified by local peculiarities, or a provincial mode of speech.

8. Baseball.
   (a) the ball
   (b) failure to hold the ball when trying to catch it
   (c) a grounder

9. "One word."

10. (a) "The Donkey Serenade"
    (b) "Ferdinand, the Bull"
    (c) "The Little Red Fox"

(2)

ANSWERS TO TELL-WHO QUIZ

1. William Henry Harrison.
2. James Whitcomb Riley.
3. Sinclair Lewis.
4. Aladdin.
5. Mark Antony.
6. Thomas A. Edison.
7. Theodore Roosevelt.
8. Geoffrey Chaucer.
9. Citizens of Boston disguised as Indians.
10. Alice, the March Hare, the Mad Hatter, and the Dormouse, all characters from *Alice in Wonderland* by Lewis Carroll.
11. Leonardo da Vinci.
12. Narcissus.
13. Sacagawea.

ANSWERS TO POPULAR QUIZ NUMBER FOUR

1. Honesty. Lincoln was called "Honest Abe." Washington was too honest to tell his father a lie.
2. Benjamin Disraeli, later Lord Beaconsfield.
3. T 4 2 ("Tea for Two")
4. Aquacade.
5. $1.21.
6. Popcorn. When it is popped, corn turns inside out.
7. Kansas.
8. (a) The name has become synonymous with "lady killer." Don Juan is the hero of dramas by Molière and Byron and of Mozart's opera.
   (b) A dungeon is a dark underground prison.
9. Pearl Buck, novelist.
   Frank Buck, animal hunter.
10. *The Grapes of Wrath.*

ANSWERS TO POPULAR QUIZ NUMBER FIVE

1. It would be noon. The airplane would be traveling at the same speed as the sun.

(3)

2. The stepsister would not be related to you, but would be the child of your stepmother or stepfather by a former marriage.
The half sister would be related to you through either your father or mother.

3. (a) Backgammon
   (b) Chess
   (c) Chinese Checkers

4. They were all defeated candidates for the Presidency of the United States.

5. "Philadelphia Story" and "Kitty Foyle."

6. Cadets at West Point can have neither wife nor automobile.

7. *A Connecticut Yankee in King Arthur's Court* by Mark Twain.

8. (a) howl
   (b) bray
   (c) gobble

9. An error. "Error" is defined as a fault of a player on the side in the field, which prolongs the time at bat of the batsman, or allows a base runner to advance one or more bases when a perfect play would have put him out.

10. "Peach Melba" was named for Nellie Melba, an opera star of Australian birth.
"Chicken Tetrazzini" was named for Luisa Tetrazzini, an opera star of Italian birth.

ANSWERS TO WHAT QUIZ

1. The saros period represents the period of time that elapses between the start of the cycle of the sun, moon, and earth and the time they return to the same relative positions. It is eighteen years and eleven and one-third days.

2. 2nd Lieut., Single Gold Bar worn on each shoulder.
1st Lieut., Single Silver Bar worn on each shoulder.
Captain, Double Silver Bars worn on each shoulder.
Major, Gold Maple Leaf worn on each shoulder.
Lieut. Col., Silver Maple Leaf worn on each shoulder.
Col., Silver Eagle worn on each shoulder.
Brig. Gen., One Silver Star worn on each shoulder.
Maj. Gen., Two Silver Stars worn on each shoulder.
Lieut. Gen., Three Silver Stars worn on each shoulder.
General, Four Silver Stars worn on each shoulder.

3. The North and the South Poles.

4. The one-hoss shay.

5. Jericho.
6. Blindness.
7. Salmon.
8. In peace time, they are used to test for gas in mines.
   In war time, they are used to test for gas in trenches.
9. Charles Darwin.
10. KDKA, Pittsburgh, Pennsylvania.
11. Will Rogers. Born in Indian Territory, died in Alaska.
12. North-northeast.
13. Buffalo at the west, and Troy and Albany at the east.
14. Mississippi.
15. A mass of floating seaweed in the North Atlantic Ocean.
16. Union of South Africa.
17. Silver.
18. A written official agreement.
19. Archer fish. It sends drops of water upward out of its mouth into the air, aiming at insects.

ANSWERS TO POPULAR QUIZ NUMBER SIX

1. The flag of the Confederacy.
2. (a) Helen Hunt Jackson
   (b) Andrew Jackson
3. (a) Walt(er) Disney
   (b) Walter Winchell
   (c) Walter Chrysler
4. Benjamin Franklin.
5. Mercury.
6. 20, 21, 22.
7. Datum.
8. The letter "X."
9. A galley ship armed for hostilities.
10. Lisbon, Portugal.

ANSWERS TO POPULAR QUIZ NUMBER SEVEN

1. The throne of England. She is the second daughter of King George VI and Queen Elizabeth.

2. Sheep.
   (a) "Baa, Baa, Black Sheep"
   (b) "Mary Had a Little Lamb"
   (c) "Little Bo-Peep"
3. Nova Scotia.
4. (a) "Remember the Maine."
   (b) "54-40 or Fight."
5. Eleven hours and fifty-six minutes.
6. Chief Justice of the United States Supreme Court. He was commissioned on January 31, 1801.
7. (a) second hand
   (b) minutes
   (c) stem
8. Thomas Hardy.
9. (a) Christmas
   (b) Halloween
   (c) Independence Day (Fourth of July)
10. Pittsburgh *Pirates*, Boston *Bees*, and New York *Giants*.

ANSWERS TO FIGURE IT OUT

1. Twenty-seven. When she turned around, the same babies that had been on her left were now on her right, so she kissed the lucky babies twice.
2. Twenty-eight minutes. If he doubled the number he put in each minute, it would be half full at the end of 29 minutes, one-quarter full at the end of 28 minutes.
3. $1,342,177.27.
4. None. Acorns grow on oak trees.
5. He put an "S" before the Roman numeral IX. Result: SIX.

ANSWERS TO POPULAR QUIZ NUMBER EIGHT

1. Antarctic.
2. *All Quiet on the Western Front.*
3. (a) Soviet Russia
   (b) Japan
   (c) England
4. The pigeon.
5. $73.10. 1940 was leap year.

6. White is the color seen when sunlight is reflected without absorption of the visible rays of the spectrum. Black is the darkest of all colors, having little or no power to reflect light.
7. George Burns, Bob Burns.
8. It is impossible to be one-sixth Indian. You would have to be ½, ¼, ¾, etc. Indian, according to the laws of heredity.
9. D K (decay).
10. Journalism.

ANSWERS TO POPULAR QUIZ NUMBER NINE

1. The Declaration of Independence and the Constitution of the United States.
2. One.
3. (a) equine
   (b) canine
4. One billion. 1,000,000,000.
5. Scotland.
6. "God Bless America."
7. "I" is the ninth letter in the alphabet. "I" is a pronoun.
8. John Barrymore, the actor.
9. *Little Women* by Louisa M. Alcott.
10. One o'clock. It should strike once. Instead, it strikes twelve, or eleven times more than it should strike.

ANSWERS TO POPULAR QUIZ NUMBER TEN

1. Kangaroo. A marsupial is an animal having a pouch for carrying the young.
2. (a) Eugene Field
   (b) Robert Frost
   (c) Edgar A. Guest
3. Abraham Lincoln and Jefferson Davis were born in Kentucky.
4. Bathysphere. It is a kind of diving sphere used for deep-sea diving.
5. Union Army of the Civil War, Confederate Army of the Civil War, and Redcoats of the British Army in the Revolutionary War.
6. "I'd rather be right than be President," said Henry Clay.
   "Speak softly, but carry a big stick," said Theodore Roosevelt.

7. Simon Legree.
8. A water jacket for cooling cylinders, a covering for the engine, and an apparatus for reducing noise from the exhaust.
9. Numbers not divisible by any number without remainder, except themselves and unity.
10. When it is hay. (John Hay)

ANSWERS TO POPULAR QUIZ NUMBER ELEVEN

1. John Greenleaf Whittier.
2. The Battle of Quebec.
3. An act passed by the British Parliament in 1774 to provide a government for the Province of Canada, extending its territory to include the Northwest Territory. The act recognized the Roman Catholic Church and the French civil law.
4. Mt. Columbia. Both Mt. Thielson and Mt. Hood are in Oregon, while Mt. Columbia is in Canada.
5. Because an elephant lives to be quite old—from 100 to 200 years. Methuselah is said to have lived 969 years.
6. Into a woodland or grassland. It is a type of fungi.
7. Rachel, the great French tragedian. Rachel, the favorite wife of Jacob.
8. 600.
9. To burn the midnight oil, to burn the candle at both ends, to burn one's bridges behind one, and to burn up the road.
10. Spanish and Portuguese.

ANSWERS TO MIGHT-HAVE-BEEN WANT ADS

1. Benjamin Franklin.
2. Leaning tower of Pisa.

ANSWERS TO POPULAR QUIZ NUMBER TWELVE

1. I, V, X, L, C, D, and M.
2. (a) a pickpocket
   (b) a gangster's sweetheart
   (c) an attorney
3. Five dozen. 360 divided by 6 equals 60.

4. (a) a ship used by the Duke and Duchess of Windsor on a visit to the United States; also a constellation seen only from the Southern Hemisphere.
   (b) a type of finch
   (c) a radio announcer
5. The letter "L."
6. (a) France. It is made of goose liver and truffles.
   (b) Hawaii. It is made of fermented taro root paste.
   (c) Russia. It is the prepared and salted roe of the sturgeon.
7. A submarine.
8. A prie-dieu is a desk for kneeling at prayers. A billet-doux is a love message.
9. Kilo.
10. To cry down, cry quits, a far cry, in full cry, to cry over spilt milk, and cry-baby. Any others you name may be counted correct.

ANSWERS TO THIS-AND-THAT QUIZ

1. No. It is an insecticide for spraying trees, etc.
2. Cellulose, either wood or cotton. A viscous solution of modified cellulose is forced through very small holes and the filament is dried.
3. No. It is a lie detector and is used in detecting criminals and wrongdoers.
4. Water at 130 degrees. Water at 30 degrees would be ice.
5. Theoretically, no, since length is the name applied to the greater of the two dimensions.
6. White. It is composed of the prismatic colors.
7. Yes. It is salt.
8. The fanning of the air supplies the flame with more oxygen, and oxygen is the essential element in combustion.
9. There is no answer. Cold is merely lack of heat.
10. To dissipate static electricity.
11. They are both produced by the same process, fire being rapid oxidation and rust slow oxidation of a material.
12. TNT.
13. It will remain the same.
14. Four. A hand being a unit of measure.
15. It would weigh the same whether hot or cold.

16. The chances are even. There are only two sides to the coin, and it must be one or the other.
17. Bronze: copper and tin. Glass: silica (sand) and an alkali (sodium or potassium). Nylon: coal, air, and water.
18. Iron rusts. Silver tarnishes. Copper corrodes.
19. Because there are 7,000 grains in an avoirdupois pound and only 5,760 grains in an apothecaries' pound.
20. Frozen helium gas. It is 272 degrees below zero Centigrade or 458 degrees below zero Fahrenheit. It is within one degree of absolute zero.

ANSWERS TO POPULAR QUIZ NUMBER THIRTEEN

1. (a) Prussia
   (b) Russia
2. The elephant.
3. (a) rubbing noses
   (b) outstretched-hand salute
4. No. Once started, the National Anthem must be played through the finish.
5. (a) There are seven lines.
   (b) They are waved.
6. Edward G. Robinson and Bill Robinson.
7. Two minutes. It will take the length of the train one minute to get into the tunnel and another minute to get out.
8. Ice hockey.
9. Albert or Leopold.
10. Kitchen Police.

ANSWERS TO POPULAR QUIZ NUMBER FOURTEEN

1. Kitty Foyle. From the book *Kitty Foyle* by Christopher Morley.
2. (a) delegate
   (b) frigate
   (c) agate
3. Golf, fishing, and fencing.
4. Neither. The Rock of Gibraltar faces on the Atlantic Ocean and the Mediterranean Sea.
5. N O. Turned around they spell "on."

6. Seven. Jefferson, Madison, Jackson, W. H. Harrison, Johnson, B. Harrison, and Wilson.
7. Sixty years old.
8. Quarter notes are completely black; half notes are outlined.
9. (a) France (Joan of Arc)
   (b) Greece (Homer)
   (c) Russia (Rasputin)
10. A passenger.

ANSWERS TO WHO, WHAT, WHERE, WHEN AND WHICH

1. In the British Empire in 1833.
2. George Washington.
3. A great wooden horse which was filled with soldiers.
4. No. It is a whip with nine lashes.
5. The Bill of Rights.
6. William Henry Harrison.
7. Queen Victoria ruled England for 64 years.
8. The bat.
9. Over the grave of Francis Scott Key in Washington.
10. When it is turned into a pasture!!!!
11. A: one dot, one dash. B: one dash, three dots. C: one dash, one dot, one dash, one dot.
12. Third base.
13. Sherlock Holmes.
14. Sixty-four.
15. One half.
16. A watch of two hours on shipboard. There are two of them: 4 to 6 and 6 to 8 P.M.
17. Both were blind.
18. Football. The games on New Year's Day.
19. Washington and Baltimore.
20. The right side.
21. The dates.
22. The United States Census.

23. Napoleon III was the nephew of Napoleon I. He was the third son of Louis Bonaparte, brother of Napoleon I.
24. The oboe.

ANSWERS TO POPULAR QUIZ NUMBER FIFTEEN

1. (a) literature (novelist)
   (b) aviation (inventor of practical flying machines)
   (c) medicine (English physician and pathologist)
2. Stepfather. John and Martha Parke Custis were children of Martha Washington by a former marriage.
3. Stalactite, for it hangs from the ceiling of the cave. A stalagmite is formed on the floor of the cave.
4. (a) throw in the sponge, give up the ship, say die
   (b) face the music, hold the bag, take it, get it in the neck
   (c) put it on the cuff
5. Harrow. It has teeth.
6. World War I.
7. A monkey wrench is a wrench having a straight handle, one fixed jaw at right angles to the handle, and one adjustable jaw.
   An alligator wrench is a wrench having a flaring jaw with teeth on one side.
8. (a) Boots
   (b) glass slipper
   (c) winged sandals
9. A portrait of Frederick the Great. Frederick the Great sent his own portrait to George Washington.
10. The Fly saw him die; the Rook was the parson; and the Thrush sang a psalm.

ANSWERS TO POPULAR QUIZ NUMBER SIXTEEN

1. (a) a rake
   (b) a basket
   (c) scales
2. O-hi-O.
3. St. George.

4. (a) Jonathan
   (b) Baldwin
   (c) Northern Spy
5. No two snowflakes are ever alike. No two fingerprints are ever alike.
6. Yes. A prune is a type of plum that is dried.
7. (a) that BURNS me up
   (b) great SCOTT
   (c) PAYNE in the neck
8. "The Night Before Christmas." Up the chimney he (St. Nick) rose. "Little Orphan Annie." The goblins got him (the little boy).
9. (a) Miami, Florida
   (b) New Orleans, Louisiana
   (c) Dallas, Texas
10. (a) corn
    (b) eggplant
    (c) beets

ANSWERS TO POPULAR QUIZ NUMBER SEVENTEEN

1. (a) Moscow, Russia
   (b) London, England
   (c) Philadelphia, Pennsylvania
2. (a) 8 (ate)
   (b) 1 (won)
   (c) 2 (too)
3. Sinclair Lewis, Howard Lindsay, and Thornton Wilder. You may count any others you name correct.
4. (a) Mockingbird
   (b) Crow
   (c) Raven
5. (a) Dime
   (b) Nickel
   (c) Penny
6. (a) Ethan Allen
   (b) Theodore Roosevelt
7. (a) George Washington
   (b) Joseph Haydn
   (c) Mississippi River
8. Yes. Plumbago is graphite or a soft, black native carbon.

9. (a) Yankee Doodle
   (b) Simple Simon
   (c) Little Polly Flinders
10. Yes, you could wear a rain hat during a strong wind from the southwest.

ANSWERS TO VARIETY QUIZ

1. British Columbia, Alberta, Saskatchewan, Manitoba, Ontario, Quebec, New Brunswick, Nova Scotia, and Prince Edward Island.
2. It is in New York Harbor and is famous because the Statue of Liberty is located there.
3. Red.
4. Ore.
5. No. It is the United States naval station in the Hawaiian Islands. The Pearl Isles are located south and slightly east of the Panama Canal.
6. Olympus.
7. "The Bells" by Edgar Allan Poe.
8. "The Ugly Duckling" by Hans Christian Andersen.
9. April, August, December, February, January, July, June, March, May, November, October, and September.
10. The chestnut tree.
11. Arizona was admitted to the Union in 1912.
12. No. Barbary Coast is a name for the coast of California. Barbary States are the countries in North Africa that lie along the southern shore of the Mediterranean Sea.
13. Connecticut.
14. There are no bricks in a cement wall.
15. January 20, 1937.
16. Abstemious or facetious.
17. Chicago.
18. No. It is gold or silver in bars or ingots.
19. Hampton Roads, Virginia, during the Civil War.

ANSWERS TO POPULAR QUIZ NUMBER EIGHTEEN

1. (a) Pinochle
   (b) Bridge
   (c) Chess

2. Four cents.
3. The subject would probably have been art forms, all three being artists, though of different schools.
4. Franklin Delano Roosevelt.
5. The process of submitting to the electorate, for approval or rejection, measures passed upon or proposed by the legislative body.
6. (a) sheep
   (b) mittens
7. The King of gems is the diamond; the Queen is the pearl.
8. Robbery is the theft of property from the person or immediate presence of another, accomplished by force or by putting him in fear.
   Burglary is the breaking into and entering of a building, in the nighttime, with intent to commit a felony. In many States the definition of the crime has been modified to cover such offenses committed by day.
9. Summer.
10. (a) zebra
    (b) Zola
    (c) Zeppelin

ANSWERS TO POPULAR QUIZ NUMBER NINETEEN

1. Sixpence. The rhyme is "Sing a Song of Sixpence."
2. Jacob and his son Joseph, who was next to the youngest.
3. Queen Elizabeth (Elizabethan) and Queen Victoria (Victorian).
4. In sub-zero weather, a refrigerator would keep food from freezing.
5. The date of Easter varies. It is always the first Sunday after the first full moon that falls on or next after the vernal equinox (March 21 in the Gregorian calendar); if the full moon happens on Sunday, Easter is celebrated one week later.
6. He can untwist the rope, dividing it into two halves of twenty-five feet each. When he ties these two together, he will have enough rope to reach the ground easily.
7. The frog. It starts life as a tadpole, having a tail and no legs, and ends life as a frog, having legs and no tail.
8. Minnesota.
9. Chrysler, Dodge, Oldsmobile, Ford, Packard and Willys.
10. James Madison. War of 1812.

ANSWERS TO POPULAR QUIZ NUMBER TWENTY

1. Helen of Troy.
2. All edible fowl, hair, windows, lumber, stone, leather, wounds, etc. You may count any others you name right.
3. President Roosevelt is the oldest. Born 1882.
   King George is the youngest. Born 1895.
   Mussolini was born in 1883.
   Hitler was born in 1889.
4. When a top is at the acme of its gyration, it becomes so steady and quiet that it does not seem to move. At this state it is said to sleep.
5. (a) *Supper*
   (b) *Water Jug*
   (c) *Sistine*
6. Peas, corn, and green lima beans.
7. The end facing in the direction which the car is headed is the front of a box car.
8. The tone volume.
9. Airplane.
10. The moon.

ANSWERS TO FILL-IN QUIZ

1. New Orleans, Louisiana.
2. Alabama and Georgia.
3. Southerly.
4. "Old Hickory."
5. Sea horse, sawhorse, clotheshorse, rocking horse, Charley horse, etc.
6. Rowing, tug of war, and backstroke swimming.
7. George V, Edward VIII, and George VI, all in 1936.
8. Thirteen stars arranged in a circle.
9. Analyst. Annalist.
10. Virginia.
11. Alexander Hamilton was killed in a duel with Aaron Burr.
12. The Diet of Worms.
13. Havana Harbor in 1898.
14. Charles Chaplin.
15. Glutton.

16. Harvard.
17. Abraham Lincoln.
18. The British.
19. Zodiac.

ANSWERS TO POPULAR QUIZ NUMBER TWENTY-ONE

1. No. Absolute pitch in a person is the ability to identify any sounded tone of an instrument, or to match with the voice any note of the scale without having first heard it.
2. (a) *Gulliver's Travels*
   (b) *Robinson Crusoe*
   (c) *Rip Van Winkle*
3. (a) cords, ropes, or cables
   (b) metal
   (c) wood
4. There are more white sheep than there are black.
5. Lambeth Walk, Cakewalk, and Camel Walk. You may count any others you name correct.
6. A fish in a swinging couch on a rounded hill under a tree.
7. A sailor. He would be singing a song as he used a mending kit.
8. No. A census board is concerned with the business of enumerating population. A board of censors is concerned with judging the propriety or fitness of things, especially publications, movies, shows, etc.
9. (a) Kansas City, Missouri
   (b) Superior, Wisconsin
   (c) Oakland, California
10. No. "The Pearl of the Antilles" is a name often given Cuba.

ANSWERS TO POPULAR QUIZ NUMBER TWENTY-TWO

1. Bowling. One shoe sole is made of leather, the other of rubber.
2. Buoyancy.
3. Alfred E. Smith is the wearer of the brown derby. The Brown Derby is a restaurant in Hollywood, California.
4. One year. Leases are for 99 years.
5. Switzerland.
6. Yes, or you could call it an autobiography.

7. (a) palm
   (b) fir (fur)
8. The construction of a building.
9. As a travelogue.
10. Making maps.

ANSWERS TO POPULAR QUIZ NUMBER TWENTY-THREE

1. The word is mite.
   (a) item
   (b) emit
   (c) time
2. Track. Both Munski and Fenske are runners.
3. Green, White, Blue Ridge, and Black mountains.
4. (a) Johann Sebastian Bach
   (b) Christoph Wilibald von Gluck
5. The Po River would remind you of Edgar Allan Poe.
6. A simple fee. A fee simple is an estate of inheritance in land without limitations.
7. (a) J, for John Jay
   (b) D, for Frances Dee
   (c) K, for "K"
8. Because it makes ma mad. Ma plus d equals mad.
9. Twenty. Twice 8 is 16; plus 20 is 36. Twice 28 is 56. 36 from 56 is 20.
10. (a) "Old MacDonald Had a Farm"
    (b) "Brother, Can You Spare a Dime"
    (c) "Yes, Sir! That's My Baby" or "You Must Have Been a Beautiful Baby"

ANSWERS TO POPULAR QUIZ NUMBER TWENTY-FOUR

1. Fahrenheit: boiling, 212 degrees; freezing, 32 degrees.
   Centigrade: boiling, 100 degrees; freezing, 0 degrees.
   Reaumur: boiling, 80 degrees; freezing, 0 degrees.
2. (a) an oboe, a wood-wind instrument
   (b) a waiter's assistant in a restaurant
   (c) an infantryman of the United States Army, also a dumpling of raised dough
3. Gainsborough's painting is *The Blue Boy;* Field's poem and the nursery rhyme are both titled "Little Boy Blue."

(18)

4. Green. Envy. We say "green with envy."
5. (a) yachting
   (b) card playing
   (c) blindman's buff
6. (a) leave without permission
   (b) one who takes back his gift
   (c) very little, or no chance
7. Twelve thousand, one hundred and eleven ($12,111).
8. The principles of morality, cosmology, social order, government, and ethics as taught by Confucius, and forming the basis for Chinese jurisprudence and education. Confucius was not the founder, but the transmitter of these teachings.
9. You would never reach the wall by that method, *theoretically*. *Practically*, you would. In the method described in the question, you would continue to halve the distance to the wall and the fraction would continue to infinity.
10. The wireless telegraph.

ANSWERS TO FIGURE FUN

1. Twenty-five. (3 times 7 plus 4 equals 25)
2. There were 5 boys and he had a total of 19¢.
3. Booth Tarkington wrote the novel *Seventeen*. 1492 divided by 2 is 746. 7 plus 4 plus 6 equals 17.
4. It would make no difference. Interest would be $30 either way.
5. $20 profit. These were two separate transactions.
6. You would have four more thumbs than fingers; twelve thumbs and eight fingers.
7. Four.
8. Four days.
9. 1,000 acres. The other end of the rope wasn't tied to anything!!!!

ANSWERS TO POPULAR QUIZ NUMBER TWENTY-FIVE

1. Delaware, Illinois, Iowa, and the Dakotas.
2. (a) Belgium
   (b) Scotland
   (c) Spain

3. The Puritans. The Puritan members of Parliament during the reign of Charles I, and later, were so called because they wore their hair short.
4. (a) Nathaniel Hawthorne
   (b) Artemus Ward
   (c) Thomas Hood
5. Alabama, Georgia, North Carolina, Virginia, Kentucky, Missouri, Arkansas, and Mississippi.
6. Cashew nut.
7. The ordinary needle has the eye at the blunt end, while the sewing machine needle has the eye near the sharp end.
8. No. It is an undesirable image that appears on the screen usually as a result of wave reflection.
9. (a) The Barretts
   (b) Phoebe Throssel
   (c) The Kennicotts
10. (a) cow
    (b) cat
    (c) horse

ANSWERS TO POPULAR QUIZ NUMBER TWENTY-SIX

1. Benjamin Disraeli, a prime minister of England during the reign of Queen Victoria, was made the Earl of Beaconsfield in 1868.
2. (a) Mark Antony
   (b) Solomon
   (c) "barefoot, bashful beau"
3. "Franklin D. Roosevelt Jones," "Ben Bolt," "Sailing on the Henry Clay," "On the Robert E. Lee," and "John Brown's Body." There may be others.
4. Chain mail is a flexible armor of interlocked metal links. Chain letters are written communications designed to pass from one to another of a series of recipients.
5. New York, with a population of 13,479,142.
   Pennsylvania, with a population of 9,900,180.
   Illinois, with a population of 7,897,241.
6. Curiosity killed a cat.
7. Eight inches. When the first book is placed beside the second book, its first page is on the side of the book which is adjacent to the second book. In other words, it is one inch in from the beginning of the row. Likewise, the last page of the last book is one inch in from the end of the row. *Try it!*

8. Ellery Queen.
9. Usher. The five pronouns are: "U," us, she, he, and her.
10. No. A calico horse is one marked with conspicuous patches of color. The gingham dog and the calico cat were stuffed toy animals.

ANSWERS TO POPULAR QUIZ NUMBER TWENTY-SEVEN

1. *Seventeen* by Booth Tarkington, and *1919* by John Dos Passos.
2. California.
3. Novel and playwriting.
4. (a) Christopher Morley
   (b) Warwick Deeping
   (c) Mrs. Kate Lee (Langley) Bosher
5. "A man of words and not of deeds."
6. John James Audubon and Benjamin Franklin.
7. Probably not. You would be in prison.
8. Wicked behavior. It applies especially to misconduct in public office.
9. (a) Galento
   (b) Godoy
   (c) Nova
10. Minnesota.

ANSWERS TO POPULAR QUIZ NUMBER TWENTY-EIGHT

1. E.
2. (a) Victor Hugo
   (b) Victor Herbert
   (c) Victor Emmanuel of Italy
3. (a) Plymouth, Massachusetts
   (b) Niagara Falls, New York
   (c) Michigan
4. Twelve.
5. They are the same. All are units of measure and are equal to 5½ yards in length.
6. An egg. It grew into a chicken.
7. By coin. And don't try to figure how much room it would take up.
8. An ode or song for one voice, a monotonous or mournful sound.

9. (a) "Silver Threads Among the Gold"
   (b) "Sweet Genevieve"
   (c) "The Man on the Flying Trapeze"
10. Colt pistol, Otis elevator, Goodyear tire, and Bell telephone.

ANSWERS TO TWO'S AND THREE'S

1. William Wordsworth, Samuel Taylor Coleridge, and Robert Southey.
2. Whippoorwill, bobwhite, cuckoo, killdeer, bobolink.
3. Edouard Manet, Claude Monet, Pierre Auguste Renoir, Paul Cézanne, etc.
4. Santa Claus, Uncle Sam, John Bull, Davy Jones, and the Man in the Moon.
5. *Niña, Pinta,* and the *Santa Maria.*
6. Bones and brows.
7. "The *dish* ran away with the *spoon.*"
   "Licked the *platter* clean."
   "Chopped off their tails with a *carving knife.*"
8. Augusta, Maine; Atlanta, Georgia; Albany, New York; Austin, Texas; Annapolis, Maryland.
9. Damon and Pythias.
10. Cloth, pie, and hose.
11. By a walk and by being hit by a pitched ball.
12. Locksmith, blacksmith, tinsmith, whitesmith, coppersmith, and goldsmith.
13. Singlefoot, canter, pace, gallop, and trot.
14. Jefferson, July 4, 1826; John Adams, July 4, 1826; Monroe, July 4, 1831.
15. As a band worn around the waist; a special area; a band on a machine; a row of plates around the waterline on a ship; a narrow strait.
16. Buffalo, deer, and antelope.
17. Beethoven, Bach, and Brahms.
18. Bismarck, North Dakota; Pierre, South Dakota; Jefferson City, Missouri.
19. Chapel——apple; beach——peach; thumb——plum.

ANSWERS TO POPULAR QUIZ NUMBER TWENTY-NINE

1. (a) the goddess of the dawn in classical mythology
   (b) the northern lights, a luminous phenomenon of light in the arctics
   (c) the southern lights, comparable to the northern lights

2. When he married Beatrice. Benedict refers to a newly married man, especially one long a bachelor.
3. (a) Russian
   (b) Japanese
   (c) Mexican
4. Anemia. Amnesia is loss of memory.
5. Charles Bonaparte was the grandson of Jerome Bonaparte, King of Westphalia.
6. William McKinley, Theodore Roosevelt, and William Taft.
7. One half dollar, one quarter, and four dimes.
8. Henry and Henry Wadsworth Longfellow.
9. No. A prairie dog is a small burrowing rodent.
10. Parchment.

ANSWERS TO POPULAR QUIZ NUMBER THIRTY

1. (a) Ferdinand Foch
   (b) Ferdinand de Lesseps
   (c) Ferdinand Magellan
2. Petrified, by fear.
3. (a) "The Old Oaken Bucket"
   (b) "Sweet and Low"
   (c) "When You and I Were Young, Maggie"
4. They were all raised from the dead by Christ.
5. Uncas. He was made famous by James Fenimore Cooper in *The Last of the Mohicans*.
6. The 16th. It provides for the tax on incomes.
7. Ten cents.
8. A Y. Bay, jay, and hay.
9. Salvador does not touch the Caribbean Sea, and British Honduras does not touch the Pacific Ocean.
10. Q, Z, and K.

ANSWERS TO TRUE OR FALSE

1. True.
2. False. Diogenes looked for the honest man.
3. False. You would be suffering from diabetes.

(23)

4. True.
5. False. The salmon is so noted.
6. True.
7. False. Millet did.
8. True.
9. True.
10. False. There are 6% more boys born.
11. True.
12. False. There are six white stripes and seven red.
13. False. A hangar is a shelter for housing airplanes, balloons, and dirigibles. A hanger belongs in a clothes closet.
14. False. It is an object of dislike or dread.
15. True.
16. True.
17. True. No one knew when Christ was to be born.
18. True.
19. False. It is a photographic or musical composite.
20. False. It never appears.

ANSWERS TO POPULAR QUIZ NUMBER THIRTY-ONE

1. At the framing of the Treaty of Versailles.
2. Slice an eighth from each piece of candy. There would be seven eighths for the eighth KID, and each piece would be seven-eighths its original size.
3. Chili today. Hot tamale (tomorrow).
4. January 1st, 2001 to December 31st, 2001.
5. Switzerland has no navy.
6. "In the beginning God created the heaven and the earth."
7. Daisy is Donald Duck's girl friend. Daisy also is the name of Blondie's dog.
8. Swimming. It is a speed stroke. A trudgen is also a speed stroke in swimming.
9. (a) ton
   (b) cord
   (c) barrel or gallon
   (d) cubic feet
10. Juliet in the play *Romeo and Juliet*.

ANSWERS TO POPULAR QUIZ NUMBER THIRTY-TWO

1. 78
2. (a) Sweet
   (b) Remember
   (c) Purpose
3. It includes northern Scandinavia and a part of northern Russia. Its area is about 150,000 square miles.
4. (a) A. Conan Doyle
   (b) Nathaniel Hawthorne
5. A player might have been stealing a base.
6. Methuselah. He is supposed to have lived 969 years.
7. James Boswell (1740–1795) was the biographer of Samuel Johnson. He recorded about a hundred incidents and conversations between himself and Johnson, whom he hero-worshiped. It means to hero-worship another and to record his actions and words, especially in print.
8. The Earl of Derby.
9. A great constitution.
10. The fourth estate is the press, or newspaper personnel.

ANSWERS TO POPULAR QUIZ NUMBER THIRTY-THREE

1. A "Pollyanna" is a person of irrepressible optimism who finds only good in everything, even misfortune.
2. The teddy bear. Named after Theodore Roosevelt.
3. A type of tractor.
4. (a) heaven or the hereafter
   (b) peace conference
   (c) end a fight
5. The bugle. It is a brass-wind instrument. The others are wood-wind instruments.
6. Benjamin Franklin. This almanac had 75 English editions, 56 French, 11 German, and 9 Italian by 1900.
7. In the ear. It is the semicircular canal which is the group of loop-shaped tubular parts of the labyrinth of the ear.
8. Dolly Madison.
9. Yale University. It was named for Elihu Yale (1648–1721).

10. Baseball. It is a form of hit-and-run play in which, when there is a runner on third base and only one out, the batter bunts a pitched ball, and the runner starts for home plate as soon as the pitcher makes a motion to pitch that ball.

ANSWERS TO WHAT QUIZ II

1. Underground.
2. James G. Blaine.
3. The adoption of the Stars and Stripes by the Continental Congress, June 14, 1777.
4. They were both Roman emperors.
5. Hellespont.
6. Doodling.
7. A vivarium is any place where any living animal is kept, such as a zoo. An aquarium is a place where only living aquatic animals are kept.
8. The typewriter, invented in 1867 by Christopher Sholes.
9. It is a valve used for the accurate control of the flow of a liquid, as in making the spray or jet in a carburetor.
10. The Treaty of Versailles.
11. They are all nonexistent.
12. They are all forms of carbon.
13. Bookkeeping.
14. The fish that caught Jonah.
15. Tennessee, Virginia, and Kentucky.
16. Nothing.
17. They are both on the Rio Grande.
18. The required number of sharps or flats placed at the beginning of a musical composition.
19. A doorbell or telephone.
20. Rhode Island.
21. They are all types of shoes.

ANSWERS TO POPULAR QUIZ NUMBER THIRTY-FOUR

1. 360 miles. The slow train had a 120-mile start. Picking up an extra 20 miles each hour, the fast train would catch up in 6 hours.
2. No. It is correct to say either "none of us has," or "none of us have."

3. Cow. California, Oregon, and Washington.
4. A simoom. All three are strong winds, but the simoom is violent and dust-laden.
5. Joe Louis and a boxing match.
6. (a) stick candy
   (b) milk chocolate, butter creams
   (c) jawbreaker
7. The Ten Commandments, the Ten Virgins, ten pieces of silver in the Parable of the Talents, and Tithing.
   Thirty pieces of silver paid to Judas for betraying Christ.
   The Flood was caused by forty days of rain, Jesus spent forty days in the wilderness, there were three periods of forty years each in Moses' life, and in the Old Testament a generation was considered forty years.
8. Antonym. Altruism is a regard for, and devotion to, the interests of others. Egoism is the excessive love and thought of self.
9. One. After that the stomach would no longer be empty.
10. Strawberries, sugar, and cream; curds and whey; and plum cake and sugar candy.

ANSWERS TO POPULAR QUIZ NUMBER THIRTY-FIVE

1. The Five-Power Treaties (United States, England, France, Japan, and Italy) provided for limitation of naval armaments.
   The Nine-Power Treaties (United States, Great Britain, France, Japan, Italy, Netherlands, Belgium, China, and Portugal) provided for adjustment of Chinese tariffs and for the open-door policy in China.
2. (a) a unit of force
   (b) a unit of intensity of illumination
   (c) a unit of work or energy
3. It means "so it is," or "so be it." It is also an expression of hearty assent or conviction.
4. (a) English
   (b) Norwegian
   (c) French
5. Fraternal, identical, and Siamese twins.
6. It would be too large. Each measurement made with the shortened tape would read an inch too much.
7. Each contains four a's.
8. John Paul Jones.

9. New York City. It is the brilliantly lit street of Broadway.
10. Tut. King Tutankhamen, more familiarly known as King Tut. His tomb was discovered in 1922 by Howard Carter.

ANSWERS TO POPULAR QUIZ NUMBER THIRTY-SIX

1. (a) Midas or Croesus
   (b) Hercules or Atlas
   (c) Solomon
2. Classifications of birds.
3. (a) Lion
   (b) Dog
   (c) Fox
4. (a) "My Old Kentucky Home"
   (b) "Old Folks at Home"
   (c) "Home, Sweet Home"
5. "I regret that I have but one life to lose for my country," said Nathan Hale.
   "All I know is what I read in the papers," said Will Rogers.
6. Romanoffs, Hapsburgs, and Hohenzollerns.
7. (a) The aqueous envelope of the earth, including all water on the earth's surface and in the atmosphere
   (b) The gaseous envelope which surrounds the earth, meaning all the air around the earth
   (c) The solid part of the earth
8. (a) Belfast, Ireland
   (b) Belgrade, Yugoslavia
9. (a) the burning of Rome
   (b) the Chicago fire
   (c) the fire following the earthquake in San Francisco
10. (a) to arrange and adjust the sails
    (b) to cheat your neighbor
    (c) to decorate a hat

ANSWERS TO WHO, WHAT, WHERE, HOW, AND WHY

1. Twelve minutes.
2. Short.
3. A unit of speed.

(28)

4. Houston is named after Sam Houston.
5. It is a term used to describe a very learned man.
6. Carbon. It would be a diamond.
7. Rope, cord, and various coarse fabrics.
8. Cassiopeia.
9. The Wars of the Roses.
10. Peter.
11. Twelve.
12. The Oath of Hippocrates.
13. Three pig's feet.
14. It settled the question of State representation in Congress.
15. Phidippides, a Greek, raced to Athens to report the Greek victory at the Battle of Marathon; since then the term has come to mean any similar long-distance contest.
16. Clock time does not exist at the North Pole since the meridians meet there.
17. Because George Eliot was a pen name for Mary Ann Evans, a woman.
18. Cryptogam is a plant which does not produce flowers or seeds. Cryptogram is a writing in cipher.
19. The Grand Canyon of the Colorado.
20. None. She was on her maiden voyage.

ANSWERS TO POPULAR QUIZ NUMBER THIRTY-SEVEN

1. (a) Revolutionary War
   (b) Civil War
   (c) Civil War
2. Palindrome. Examples are: "Madam, I'm Adam," ere, toot, Hannah, "Lewd did I live; evil I did dwel," and oh, ho. Any others you name may be counted.
3. (a) King
   (b) Judge
   (c) Lord Chancellor
4. All three. They are kinds of fabric that can be made into clothing.
5. Wagon, shoe, bell, buckle, railroad switch, reed in a musical instrument, and a flame. Any others you name may be counted correct.
6. Mickey Rooney. Uncle Sam is an imaginary person.

7. (a) Prince Edward Island
   (b) Panama Canal Zone
8. Vermont
9. (a) Kris Kringle
   (b) Tiny Tim
10. Advanced one day.

ANSWERS TO POPULAR QUIZ NUMBER THIRTY-EIGHT

1. *Thorne Smith 3-Decker* by Thorne Smith.
2. 240 pounds. The short ton is 2,000 pounds, the long ton 2,240 pounds.
3. An old-fashioned smoothbore gun.
4. Thornton Wilder.
5. Two feet. The boat rises with the tide.
6. Maryland.
7. (a) crabmeat
   (b) clams
   (c) shrimp
8. Because they lay their eggs in salt water only.
9. Maui.
10. (a) acting
    (b) banking
    (c) composing music

ANSWERS TO POPULAR QUIZ NUMBER THIRTY-NINE

1. Wyandotte Cave in southern Indiana, Mammoth Cave, Kentucky, and Carlsbad Caverns in New Mexico.
2. (a) adjutant
   (b) crane
   (c) dipper
3. Socrates was the philosopher and Demosthenes the orator.
4. Twenty.
5. Adsorption is the adhesion of a thin layer of dissolved material or liquid to the surface of a solid body.
   Absorption is the act of one substance's taking in another and causing it to lose its identity.

6. (a) Mary, the Rose of Tralee
   (b) K-K-K-Katy
   (c) Peggy O'Neil
7. Henri Christophe became Emperor of Haiti. Aesop was the writer of fables.
8. To decorate an interior. It is a wild flower.
9. Five pounds. A cent and a quarter are twenty-six cents.
10. They are all trees, and Joyce Kilmer wrote "Trees."

ANSWERS TO QUIZZICAL QUIZZES

1. The outside.
2. Bananas.
3. Meat.
4. Four dollars.
5. Pull the plug out of the tub.
6. The yolk of an egg is yellow.
7. Selling fish. (Sell fish)
8. Strike out!!!

ANSWERS TO PICTURE PUZZLERS

Disaster at the Dock: There are five children at the dock, two girls and three boys. One little girl is in the water. One boy has caught the fishhook in his trousers, and in the excitement has tipped over the fish bucket, throwing out the two fish. One little girl smiles as a boy runs with scissors to cut the hook from the trousers. The third little boy is busy tying a lifesaver to his toy sailboat. There is a motorboat on the water and three cottages are on the distant shore.

Scrambled Pairs: 2 and 11, dog and cat; 3 and 10, June bride; 5 and 4, cop and robber; 9 and 6, boots and saddle; 7 and 12, duck and water.

Out of the Pages of Books: 1. "Alice in Wonderland"; 2. "Little Black Sambo"; 3. "Little Lord Fauntleroy"; 4. "Cinderella."

Animals from Storyland: "The Tale of Peter Rabbit"; "The Fox and the Grapes"; "The Lion and the Mouse"; "The Hare and the Tortoise"; "Black Beauty"; and "The Three Pigs."

The Absent-minded Artist: The curtains are different; the bird is inside the window; the boy has on two different socks; the girl has on two different shoes; the boy has one long and one short sleeve; "flour" has been misspelled; the rolling pin has no handle; the cabinet knobs don't match; there is only one handle on the tray; the clock has one hand; the ironing board has only one leg; there is no iron on the handle; "clothespins" has been misspelled; the girl ironing has straight hair on one side and curly on the other; the tail doesn't fit the dog; and the boy has one long and one short pants leg.

A "B" Hunt: Branches, bridge, bait, breeches, boots, bonnet, bag, buns, bottle, basket, boy, bird, bootees, bib, baby, bug, bucket, bail, bowl, beans, butterfly, bolero, boat, ball, bank, brook, bow, boulder, and blouse.